A FAMILY OF

Faith

Catechesis for the Whole Family

ACTIVITY BOOK

VOLUME I: EXPLORING THE PROFESSION OF FAITH

SOPHIA
INSTITUTE PRESS

Based on a program conceived by
Mary Mosher

Authors
Veronica Burchard
Sean Fitzpatrick
Jose Gonzalez
Michael Gutzwiller
Mary Mosher

Editors
Veronica Burchard
Carolyn McKinney

Academic Advisor
Michel Therrien, S.T.L., S.T.D.

Special Thanks
Fr. Moe Larochelle
Mary Mosher
Terry Buldoc
Suzanne Walsh

Illustrator
Mary MacArthur

Mary Mosher, catechist, founder of Holy Family Academy in Manchester, NH, and mother of five adult children who are practicing Catholics, developed and continually refined a version of this program for 24 years at Ste. Marie Parish in Manchester, NH. Mary has a Master of Arts in Theology and Christian Ministry from the Franciscan University of Steubenville with a concentration in catechetics and additionally is certified in catechetics from the Franciscan University. We could not be more grateful to Mary for her help and advice, her service to the Church, and her efforts to lead souls closer to Christ.

This supplemental resource is not eligible for review by the USCCB. It has been reviewed for doctrinal soundness by our academic and theological advisors and is currently under review for an imprimatur. The complete, four-volume series will be reviewed for conformity with Church teaching by the USCCB.

Cover Image
Icon of the Holy Family of Nazareth, inspired by Peter Murphy, written by Fabrizio Diomedi, © Peter Murphy and Fabrizio Diomedi; Photograph © Joe Gavin, Frank Gavin Photography.

Printed in the United States of America
Design by Perceptions Design Studio

A Family of Faith: Catechesis for the Whole Family Activity Book
Volume I: Exploring the Profession of Faith
ISBN: 978-1-622825-042

INSIDE

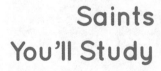
Saints You'll Study

 St. Francis of Assisi
Page 34

 St. Brigid of Ireland
Page 116

 St. Nicholas
Page 79

 St. Peter
Page 131

 St. Paul the Apostle
Page 100

 St. Catherine of Siena
Page 154

GETTING STARTED

INTRODUCTION

GOD CREATED YOU out of love, and your destiny is to go to Heaven. This is why you are here: to love Him back and live with Him forever in Heaven. Since you cannot love someone whom you do not know, the activities in this book are meant to help you understand who God is so you can grow to love Him.

You may have heard the phrase "God is love." Remember that love is not just something that God does. Love is what God is. This activity book is meant to help you know the love who is Jesus Christ. In these pages, you will learn about the Blessed Trinity: God the Father, Jesus, and the Holy Spirit; the great miracles that Jesus performed so we would know He is God, including the most awesome miracle of all – the Resurrection; the Church He founded, and how you can choose to respond to God's gift of love and go to Heaven after you die.

This activity book includes readings, coloring pages, saint stories, crafts, word searches, crossword puzzles, prayers, and other activities. As with everything in life, you will get out of these activities what you put into them.

Coloring, Drawing, and Crafts

Coloring is fun and relaxing, and also educational. You can learn a lot from a coloring page by looking at details. Who is in the picture? What are they doing? What details do you notice?

Some activities ask you to draw pictures. Drawing is not just a way to "express yourself." Rather, drawing in response to a question is a chance to develop and show your thought processes in a creative way. If you are drawing a scene, who is in it? Draw yourself in the picture. What are you doing? What are you thinking? What or whom are you listening to, or what are you saying? Think about these and other questions as you draw.

As you do crafts, examine all the pictures and symbols. Read carefully the Bible verses. Try to make something beautiful, and remember that everything that is good and beautiful and true comes from God.

Writing

Writing is an opportunity for you to reflect on your thinking and become more aware of your thought processes. Reflect on not just about what you think, but about why you think it. You might not understand everything right away. That's okay! It is good to have questions. When you ask questions, make them specific. Don't just say, "I don't understand." Instead, try to identify what it is exactly that you don't understand, and ask your question that way.

Praying

Most of all, spend time with God in prayer every day. Thank Him for all the blessings in your life, and even for your struggles. Ask the Holy Spirit to guide you. Remember that praying isn't just talking to God; it's also about listening to Him. He will speak to you in your heart; you just have to be listening. That means taking time for quiet reflection. Turn off the music, leave distractions behind, and pray.

Have a wonderful year learning about the Apostles' Creed, the Faith we profess as Catholics!

BIBLE BASICS

Fill in the blanks.

1. The Bible is divided into two parts: the _____ Testament, and the _____ Testament.

2. The Old Testament begins with the book of _____. What are the first words of this book? _____

3. The Old Testament is broken into sections: the Pentateuch, the historical books, the wisdom books, and the books of the prophets. The Pentateuch, also called the Torah by the Jews, is made up of the first _____ books of the Bible.

4. The New Testament tells the story of _____ and the New Covenant in His Blood.

5. The New Testament was written by the _____ or their immediate disciples.

6. The New Testament begins with the four Gospels: _____, _____, _____, and _____.

7. Following the Gospels is the book of _____, which tells the story of how the Apostles set up the early Church.

8. Following the book of Acts are 21 _____, or letters to particular churches in the ancient world.

9. The final book is _____, a prophecy about the Apocalypse (end-times).

Mark each item "OT" if it would be found in the Old Testament,
or "NT" if you would find it in the New Testament.

_____ 1. God created the heavens and the earth.

_____ 2. Jesus was born.

_____ 3. Jesus called the first disciples.

_____ 4. God created the first man and the first woman.

_____ 5. St. Paul wrote to the church in Corinth about what love means.

_____ 6. The first man and the first woman disobey God.

_____ 7. God gives the ancient Israelites the Ten Commandments.

_____ 8. Jesus is crucified.

_____ 9. The prophets tell the Israelites to be ready for the Messiah.

_____ 10. Jesus sends the Holy Spirit to breathe life into the Church.

_____ 11. The Book of Genesis

_____ 12. The Book of the Acts of the Apostles

_____ 13. The Book of Matthew

_____ 14. The Book of Mark

_____ 15. The Book of Luke

_____ 16. The Book of Exodus

_____ 17. The First Letter to the Corinthians

_____ 18. The Book of Proverbs

_____ 19. The Book of Isaiah

_____ 20. The Book of Revelation

BASIC CATHOLIC PRAYERS

OUR FATHER

Our Father, Who art in Heaven, hallowed be Thy name; Thy Kingdom come, Thy will be done on earth as it is in Heaven. Give us this day our daily bread; and forgive us our trespasses as we forgive those who trespass against us; and lead us not into temptation, but deliver us from evil. AMEN.

HAIL MARY

Hail Mary, full of grace. The Lord is with thee. Blessed art thou among women, and blessed is the fruit of thy womb, Jesus. Holy Mary, Mother of God, pray for us sinners, now and at the hour of our death. AMEN.

GLORY BE

Glory be to the Father, and to the Son, and to the Holy Spirit. As it was in the beginning, is now, and ever shall be, world without end. AMEN.

I BELIEVE IN GOD, THE FATHER ALMIGHTY

This month you will explore questions such as:

What does it mean to believe?

Who is God?

How can we know Him?

VERSE OF THE MONTH
HEBREWS 11:1

Faith is the realization of what is hoped for
and evidence of things not seen.

SAINT OF THE MONTH
ST. FRANCIS OF ASSISI

St. Francis lived hundreds of years ago in
Italy. He was very poor, but he was also
very happy. He loved all of God's Creation –
some say he could even talk to animals.

Learn more about him on page 34

ACT OF FAITH

O my God, I firmly believe that You are one God in three Divine Persons, Father, Son, and Holy Spirit; I believe that your Divine Son became man and died for our sins and that He will come to judge the living and the dead. I believe these and all the truths that the holy Catholic Church teaches, because You revealed them Who can neither deceive nor be deceived. Amen.

In the space below, you can practice writing this prayer or you can draw a picture of what the prayer makes you think of or how it makes you feel.

HEBREWS 11:1
SCRIPTURE MEMORIZATION

Write out this month's Bible verse on the lines below.

Faith is the realization of what is hoped for and evidence of things not seen.

WHAT IS FAITH?

Read the essay below, then talk with your parents about faith.

Faith is a gift from God, as well as our free response to believe what God tells us about Himself and about the world He made.

Faith is a gift

If faith is a gift, how do we receive it? We first receive the gift of faith in the Sacrament of Baptism. The sacraments are the chief means of receiving of God's grace in our lives. Thus, whenever we properly receive the sacraments, we receive an increase in our faith. We must also ask God, in prayer, to increase our faith. "The apostles said to the Lord, 'Increase our faith!'" (Luke 17:5).

Faith is necessary for salvation

Jesus tells us many times, and the Catholic Church teaches that "Believing in Jesus Christ and in the One who sent him for our salvation is necessary for obtaining that salvation" (CCC 161).

Our faith can be increased, but it also can be lost. We are free to accept or to reject God. We can deny His presence through our fear or doubt, and we can choose to lose His presence by our own mortal sin. God is always calling us to Himself, but He never coerces us. We must choose to believe in Him and we must live our lives according to His revealed truth.

Faith is a theological virtue

There are three theological virtues — faith, hope, and love. They are called theological virtues because they come from and point us toward God. "Faith is the theological virtue by which we believe in God and believe all that he has said and revealed to us, and that Holy Church proposes for our belief, because he is truth itself" (CCC 1814).

Faith is certain

Unlike human beings who sin, or who fail despite their best intentions, God never sins or fails. For this reason, faith is *certain*. We can be more sure of our faith in God than we can be in any human knowledge.

Our faith is not a blind leap, even though the truths that have been revealed to us are sometimes not clear to our human understanding. We believe because it is God who has revealed the truth to us.

Scripture tells us: "Faith is the realization of what is hoped for and evidence of things not seen." (Hebrews 11:1).

Since all human beings can and will fail at one time or another, we would be foolish to place all our trust in any human being. There is only One in whom we should completely trust – God. God can never fail. He alone is completely trustworthy and faithful.

FAITH AND BELIEF
SCRIPTURE SEARCH

Use your Bible to find the following verses and write them out. Then spend some time reflecting on each one before talking about them with your family.

1. Hebrews 11:1 _____

   _____

2. John 6:47 _____

   _____

3. Psalm 31:14 _____

   _____

4. Hebrews 11:6 _____

   _____

5. 2 Corinthians 5:7 _____

   _____

6. James 1:6 _____

   _____

7. John 20:29 _____

   _____

THE APOSTLES' CREED

Look for the 12 articles as you read
and pray the Apostles' Creed.

I believe in God, the Father almighty, creator of heaven and earth, and in Jesus Christ, His only Son, our Lord, who was conceived by the Holy Spirit and born of the Virgin Mary, suffered under Pontius Pilate, was crucified, died and was buried; He descended into hell; on the third day He rose again from the dead; He ascended into Heaven, and is seated at the right hand of God, the Father almighty; from there He will come to judge the living and the dead. I believe in the Holy Spirit, the holy Catholic Church, the communion of saints, the forgiveness of sins, the resurrection of the body, and life everlasting.

AMEN

HOW CAN WE KNOW GOD?

Read the essay below, then talk with your parents about the ways we can know God.

We can come to know and to believe in the existence of God in three ways: through reason, through Divine Revelation, and through God's creation.

We can know God through reason

Reason alone is not sufficient to know and love God, but we can know that He exists through reason. Faith and reason do not contradict each other. In fact, the word *theology* means faith seeking understanding. The *Catechism* teaches that although we can be certain of God through reason, there is greater knowledge that comes to us only through Divine Revelation. We can know Divine Revelation through the Word of God in the Bible, and through the Tradition of the Church Jesus founded.

We can know God through Divine Revelation

Because it was God's will that we would come to know Him, to love Him, and to live with Him eternally in Heaven, He has gradually revealed Himself to mankind. Salvation history is filled with the stories of God's mercy and His covenants with Adam, Noah, Abraham, Moses, and David. The fullness of this revelation would come to mankind in the person and mission of Jesus Christ, His only Son.

"He has made known to us the mystery of His will in accord with His favor that He set forth in Him as a plan for the fullness of times, to sum up all things in Christ, in heaven and on earth" (Ephesians 1:9-10).

This revelation has been preserved for us, and for all generations, through the Sacred Scriptures and Sacred Tradition guarded by the Magisterium (teaching authority) of the Church. Regularly spending time with God in prayer, hearing the Word of God at each Holy Mass, and receiving the Sacraments – especially Confession and Holy Communion – will help you grow in your understanding of Divine Revelation.

We can know God through His creation

The story of God's wonderful plan for all mankind begins in Genesis 1. The account of creation answers for us the most basic questions that people ask in life: where do we come from, and where are we going?

Through creation, we can see and know that there is a God. St. Paul speaks of this truth when he says, "For what can be known about God is evident to them, because God made it evident to them. Ever since the creation of the world, His invisible attributes of eternal power and divinity have been able to be understood and perceived in what He has made. As a result, they have no excuse" (Romans 1:19-20).

The human person also attests to the existence of God. Within ourselves we find truth, beauty, goodness, and a longing for that which is eternal. In this, man senses his spiritual soul – a soul that could be created only by an eternal One who is all truth, all beauty, and all goodness. In this way, man in himself gives witness to the truth of God's existence.

WHO IS GOD?

In the space below, write or draw your answer to the question: "How would you describe God?"

ATTRIBUTES OF GOD

Look up and read the Bible verses listed below,
then write them on the lines.

God is a perfect being. That means that:

1. **God is holy.** He cannot do or think anything evil.

   " _____

   _____ " (Isaiah 6:3)

2. **God is almighty.** There is nothing He cannot do.

   " _____

   _____ " (Daniel 4:32)

3. **God is omniscient, or all knowing.** He understands everything and can see all of
   His knowledge at one time.

   " _____

   _____ " (Psalm 139)

4. **God is eternal and unchanging.** He never had a beginning, and He will never
   come to an end. He does not grow and change. He is always the same.

   " _____

   _____ " (Psalm 135:13)

5. **God is omnipresent.** He is a pure spirit and has no body. Thus, He is everywhere
   all at once.

   " _____

   _____ " (Proverbs 15:3)

GOD IS BIGGER THAN OUR WORRIES

In the space below, draw a picture, compose a song, or write a prayer that shows God taking care of you and anything you are worried about.

EXPLORING THE TRINITY

A shamrock is a traditional symbol of the Trinity.

On one leaf of the shamrock write, "The Father," on another write, "The Son," and on the third write, "The Holy Spirit." Then color or decorate your symbol of the Trinity.

EXPLORING THE TRINITY

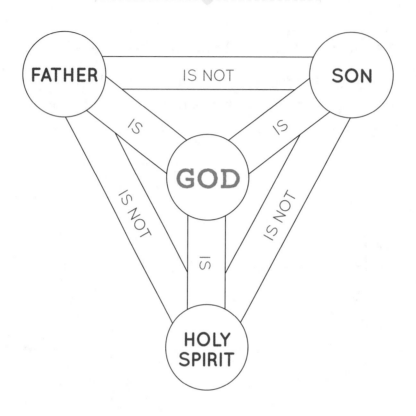

Look up the following two Scripture passages and read them aloud:

- ➤ Mark 1:10-11
- ➤ John 16:5-7, 12-15

On the lines below, tell about what you read regarding the Trinity.

_____

_____

_____

_____

_____

_____

THE STORY OF CREATION

GENESIS 1:1-2

In the beginning, when God created the heavens and the earth — and the earth was without form or shape, with darkness over the abyss and a mighty wind sweeping over the waters —

Color the dove, which is a symbol for the Spirit of God, and color the water.

GENESIS 1:3-5

Then God said: Let there be light, and there was light. God saw that the light was good. God then separated the light from the darkness. God called the light "day," and the darkness He called "night." Evening came, and morning followed – the first day.

Color the light

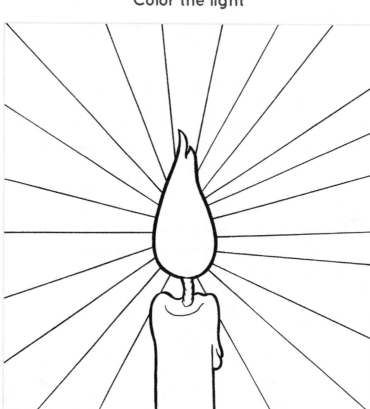

List two things that you can do when it is dark.

1. _____

2. _____

List two things that you like to do when it is light.

1. _____

2. _____

GENESIS 1:6-8

Then God said: Let there be a dome in the middle of the waters, to separate one body of water from the other. God made the dome, and it separated the water below the dome from the water above the dome. And so it happened. God called the dome "sky." Evening came, and morning followed – the second day.

Use your imagination to create a beautiful sky on this page. You can use pictures cut from magazines; you can draw the sky; or you can paste construction paper on this page to create a sky.

GENESIS 1:9-10

Then God said: Let the water under the sky be gathered into a single basin, so that the dry land may appear. And so it happened: the water under the sky was gathered into its basin, and the dry land appeared. God called the dry land "earth," and the basin of water he called "sea." God saw that it was good.

Cross out the things that you would NOT find in the waters (oceans, lakes, streams, ponds):

24

GENESIS 1:11-13

Then God said: Let the earth bring forth vegetation: every kind of plant that bears seed and every kind of fruit tree on earth that bears fruit with its seed in it. And so it happened: the earth brought forth vegetation: every kind of plant that bears seed and every kind of fruit tree that bears fruit with its seed in it. God saw that it was good. Evening came, and morning followed – the third day.

Only God can create something out of nothing. Write a prayer thanking God for all the trees, flowers, fruit, bushes, and grass that He has created. Then draw a picture of your favorite flower.

Dear Lord,

_____

_____

_____

_____

_____

_____

_____

_____

_____

GENESIS 1:14-19

Then God said: Let there be lights in the dome of the sky, to separate day from night. Let them mark the seasons, the days and the years, and serve as lights in the dome of the sky, to illuminate the earth. And so it happened: God made the two great lights, the greater one to govern the day, and the lesser one to govern the night, and the stars. God set them in the dome of the sky, to illuminate the earth, to govern the day and the night, and to separate the light from the darkness. God saw that it was good. Evening came, and morning followed – the fourth day.

Draw the moon and the stars in the sky.

GENESIS 1:20-21

Then God said: Let the water teem with an abundance of living creatures, and on the earth let birds fly beneath the dome of the sky. God created the great sea monsters and all kinds of crawling living creatures with which the water teems, and all kinds of winged birds. God saw that it was good...

Color the whale.

GENESIS 1:22-25

...and God blessed them, saying: Be fertile, multiply, and fill the water of the seas; and let the birds multiply on the earth. Evening came, and morning followed—the fifth day. Then God said: Let the earth bring forth every kind of living creature: tame animals, crawling things, and every kind of wild animal. And so it happened: God made every kind of wild animal, every kind of tame animal, and every kind of thing that crawls on the ground. God saw that it was good.

God created all the animals that live on the earth. God did not use anything to make His creation. Only God can create something out of nothing.

Pretend that God has given you the job of creating a brand new animal for Him. Draw a picture of your animal in the space below and give it a name. Where would it live, and what would it like to eat?

28

GENESIS 1:26-31

Then God said: Let us make human beings in our image, after our likeness. Let them have dominion over the fish of the sea, the birds of the air, the tame animals, all the wild animals, and all the creatures that crawl on the earth. God created mankind in His image; in the image of God He created them; male and female He created them. God blessed them and God said to them: Be fertile and multiply; fill the earth and subdue it. Have dominion over the fish of the sea, the birds of the air, and all the living things that crawl on the earth. God also said: See, I give you every seed-bearing plant on all the earth and every tree that has seed-bearing fruit on it to be your food; and to all the wild animals, all the birds of the air, and all the living creatures that crawl on the earth, I give all the green plants for food. And so it happened. God looked at everything He had made, and found it very good. Evening came, and morning followed – the sixth day.

Only God can create something out of nothing. Everything that human beings make is made using the materials or things that God made.

Take a nature walk in your yard or neighborhood and look for things that God has created. Then write down what you find on the next page — one thing for each letter of the alphabet.

CREATION NATURE WALK

As a family, go on a nature walk. Write down things you find in God's creation, one thing for each letter of the alphabet.

A. _____

B. _____

C. _____

D. _____

E. _____

F. _____

G. _____

H. _____

I. _____

J. _____

K. _____

L. _____

M. _____

N. _____

O. _____

P. _____

Q. _____

R. _____

S. _____

T. _____

U, V, W. _____

X, Y, Z. _____

GENESIS 2:2-3

On the seventh day God completed the work He had been doing; He rested on the seventh day from all the work He had undertaken. God blessed the seventh day and made it holy, because on it He rested from all the work He had done in creation.

Sunday is our day of rest. We call it the Lord's Day. God has told us to keep it holy and to use it to rest from our work. It is a special day for families — a day when we can spend time doing things together.

Circle the things that show ways in which you can keep holy the Lord's Day and set it aside for rest and family time.

THANKSGIVING PRAYER

God created all things, and He gave them to us
because He loves us so very much.

**Using words or pictures, compose a prayer of thanksgiving
to God for all the wonderful things He has created.**

ST. FRANCIS OF ASSISI
THE ONE WE ALL LOVE

ST. FRANCIS was a man who lived 700 years ago in a city called Assisi. Assisi is in a country called Italy, which is on the continent of Europe. Francis did not always live like a saint. When he was a young man, he liked to spend lots of money having parties with his friends.

Francis went to fight in a war called the Crusades. He was a good and courageous soldier, but one day the enemy caught him. They put him in jail. Francis became very sick and almost died. Soon Francis was allowed to go home, but he was still sick. While he was getting better, he began to feel very sad that he had spent so much time just having parties and spending money. Then Jesus began to speak in Francis's heart. He began to see that his life would be much better if he listened to Jesus and tried to do God's will.

Francis began to love Jesus with all his heart. God made him so joyful that he didn't need to own any possessions to be happy. He gave all of his fancy clothes and other expensive things back to his father. Then he went outside the city to live by himself. He prayed a lot, and listened in his heart to what Jesus wanted him to do.

Jesus said, "Rebuild my church." Jesus meant for Francis to rebuild the Catholic Church, but Francis thought Jesus was telling him to rebuild a church building. So he obeyed Jesus literally, and went off to find a broken-down church to fix up. The one he found was called San Damiano, outside the town of Assisi.

Francis was so joyful in his simple life that other men decided to follow him. Soon he had a group of friends who wanted to live without possessions and to love God as Francis did. Francis called this group of men the Friars Minor. They had a rule that every man must be poor and wear only a brown robe. They begged for food in the city, and they helped poor and sick people.

Since Francis loved God, he also loved all things that God had created. Though only people are created in God's image, Francis liked to call all animals his brothers and sisters. He even called the sun his brother and the moon his sister! One story about him even became a legend. A fierce wolf was attacking people in a small town nearby. The people asked Francis to help them. Francis had such a love for all creatures that he was able to talk to the wolf. He told the wolf that the townspeople would feed him, so he would not need to kill people for food. The wolf agreed, and the town was saved. No one knows for sure if this legend is true, but many people still believe it today.

Francis was not very old when he died. At the time of his death, the Friars Minor were all over Europe, and today they are the largest group of monks in the Catholic Church. We celebrate the feast of St. Francis on October 4.

ST. FRANCIS OF ASSISI

EXCERPT FROM "THE CANTICLE OF BROTHER SUN"
BY ST. FRANCIS OF ASSISI

Most High, all powerful, good Lord, Yours are the praises, the glory, the honor, and all blessing...

Be praised, my Lord, through all Your creatures, especially through my lord Brother Sun, who brings the day; and You give light through him. And he is beautiful and radiant in all his splendor! Of You, Most High, he bears the likeness.

Praised be You, my Lord, through Sister Moon and the stars, in heaven You formed them clear and precious and beautiful.

Praised be You, my Lord, through Brother Wind, and through the air, cloudy and serene, and every kind of weather through which You give sustenance to Your creatures.

Praised be You, my Lord, through Sister Water, which is very useful and humble and precious and chaste.

Praised be You, my Lord, through Brother Fire, through whom You light the night, and he is beautiful and playful and robust and strong.

Praised be You, my Lord, through Sister Mother Earth, who sustains us and governs us and who produces varied fruits with colored flowers and herbs.

AMEN

1. A *canticle* is a religious hymn or song. Whom is St. Francis praising throughout his song?

   _____

2. In this part of his canticle, St. Francis expresses his love for the sun, the moon, the wind, the water, fire, and the earth. Why do you think he chose those parts of God's creation to sing about?

   _____

   _____

3. Write your own canticle praising God. In it, tell God about your favorite parts of His creation.

   _____

   _____

   _____

   _____

   _____

   _____

WORD SEARCH

This word search includes all your Words to Know for this month. See how many you can find. Have fun!

```
S  T  N  N  B  X  G  Z  C  Y  O  O  K  D  C
K  S  R  O  G  M  S  I  R  X  O  N  Z  E  C
R  D  O  I  L  U  R  G  E  Z  Y  B  T  E  T
B  Z  M  R  N  M  N  V  A  N  U  K  X  R  Y
J  J  O  H  C  I  Z  M  T  S  F  A  B  C  E
F  K  S  M  P  E  T  S  O  R  E  B  R  S  B
H  T  I  A  F  G  H  Y  R  V  Z  P  V  E  O
M  D  P  H  M  Q  A  T  E  P  X  M  G  L  U
F  J  E  S  K  O  E  I  F  Y  B  V  Z  T  Z
Q  E  T  E  J  O  L  G  E  O  I  I  R  S  J
Y  B  J  Y  R  E  F  J  E  L  N  U  H  O  T
O  F  P  G  B  C  F  X  T  C  S  G  Q  P  X
I  M  Y  S  T  E  R  Y  F  T  D  A  I  A  E
D  F  S  R  C  A  E  U  P  J  X  N  V  S  Q
N  S  R  G  Q  W  V  B  I  L  H  L  N  I  S
```

Believe

Trust

Faith

Obey

Creed

Apostles' Creed

Mystery

Trinity

Sign of the Cross

Creator

WORDS TO KNOW

Below are the words you should know and understand after the lessons this month. Write the definition on an index card so you can remember it.

Believe	To accept as the truth.
Trust	To rely on someone.
Faith	A gift from God as well as our free response to believe what God tells us about Himself and about the world He made.
Theological Virtues	Faith, hope, and love; these virtues come from God and point to Him.
Obey	To do what God tells us to do (and to do what God's representatives – parents, priests, teachers, and so forth – tell us to do).
Creed	All the things that we believe in.
Apostles' Creed	The most important truths about our Catholic Faith written down together. These include many of the truths God wants us to have faith in.

WORDS TO KNOW

(continued)

Divine Revelation	Truths about God that we could never know on our own and that God has chosen to reveal to us.
Mystery	A truth that is above our ability to understand on our own. We believe in a mystery because God has revealed it to us.
Trinity	A mystery that tells us that there are Three Persons in one God.
Sign of the Cross	A Catholic way to begin prayer; it reminds us of our belief in the Trinity of God and in the Passion and death of His Son, Jesus.
Creator	God, who made all things. Only God can make something out of nothing.

MADE IN HIS IMAGE, BUT FALLEN FROM GRACE

This month you will explore questions such as:

What does it mean to be created in the image of God?

What happened after Adam and Eve sinned?

How can we know God keeps always His promises?

VERSE OF THE MONTH
GENESIS 1:27

God created mankind in His image; in the image of God
He created them; male and female He created them.

SAINTS OF THE MONTH
THE OLD TESTAMENT PATRIARCHS

God made special promises to Adam, Noah, Abraham, Moses, and David. Although people often broke their promises, God always kept His.

GENESIS 1:27
SCRIPTURE MEMORIZATION

Write out this month's Bible verse on the lines below.

God created mankind in His image; in the image of God He created them; male and female He created them.

PAPER FIGURE ACTIVITY

Cut out the paper figure. Then glue a circle of shiny foil over the face of the figure. What are some ways in which you reflect God in how you think? In what you say? In what you do? Write your thoughts on the paper figure.

SPIRITUAL CREATION AND MATERIAL CREATION

How does this diagram show us the unique place of man in creation?

_____

_____

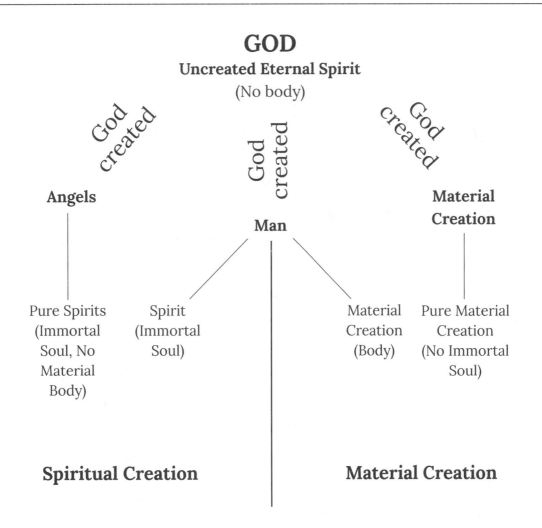

GOD
Uncreated Eternal Spirit
(No body)

God created   *God created*   *God created*

Angels   **Material Creation**

Man

Pure Spirits (Immortal Soul, No Material Body)   Spirit (Immortal Soul)   Material Creation (Body)   Pure Material Creation (No Immortal Soul)

Spiritual Creation   **Material Creation**

OUR LIFE OF GRACE

For each example your parent gives, draw a candle
with a flame that represents grace in your life.

ORIGINAL HOLINESS & JUSTICE AND THE FALL

FILL-IN-THE-BLANK

Fill in the blanks using the words in the Answer Bank.
Words may be used more than once.

Answer Bank

Holiness	Reason	Beatific Vision	Soul
Likeness	Choose freely	Spiritual	Original Sin
Love	Image	Immortal	Material
	Justice	Grace	

1. Adam and Eve were created in the _____ and _____ of God.

2. It is in Adam and Eve's _____ that they especially reflect the image of God.

3. The state in which God created Adam and Eve is called Original _____ and _____.

4. A human person's soul is _____, which means it will live forever.

5. It is in our soul that we can _____, _____, and _____.

6. In all creation, man alone is both a _____being and a _____ being.

7. The life of God in us is called _____.

8. Seeing God face-to-face in Heaven is called the _____.

9. The sin of Adam and Eve, and thus the sin of all of our beginnings, is called _____.

10. The story of salvation does not end with the Fall. The story of salvation is a _____ story.

COLORING AND ACTIVITY PAGES

NOAH, JOSEPH, AND MOSES

GOD'S PROMISE TO NOAH

Many years after Adam and Eve sinned, God was sad about how bad most people had become. God decided to flood the earth and start over. Noah was a good and faithful man. God chose Noah to build a big boat called an ark. The ark would save Noah's family and two of every animal. Afterward, God promised Noah He would never flood the earth again. The sign of His covenant was a rainbow.

Color the rainbow.

JOSEPH'S PREDICAMENT

Abraham's son Isaac grew up and had two sons: Jacob and Esau. Jacob married and was blessed with twelve sons. From these twelve sons came the twelve tribes of Israel. The Chosen People are called Israelites because later God changed Jacob's name to Israel. One of Jacob's (Israel's) sons was Joseph. Joseph's brothers sold him into slavery in Egypt. But God took their sin and turned it into good. He was keeping His promise to His Chosen People! The symbol of how God kept His promise to His people through the life of Joseph is Joseph's coat of many colors.

Read the story of Joseph in Genesis 37:3-36. Use the verses to help you unscramble the words. Then write the circled letters in order in the spaces at the bottom of the page to discover a truth about God's love.

1. Israel loved ___ ___ ___ ___ ___ ___ (SPHOJE) more than any of his sons. Verse 3

2. Joseph had a ___ ___ ___ ___ ___ (REMAD). Verse 5

3. Joseph's brothers had gone to graze their father's
    ___ ___ ___ ___ ___ ___ (KLOFCS). Verse 12

4. His brothers called Joseph a ___ ___ ___ ___ ___ ___ ___ (MARREDE). Verse 19

5. Joseph's brothers plotted to ___ ___ ___ ___ (LILK) him. Verse 20

6. They threw Joseph into a ___ ___ ___ ___ ___ ___ ___ (TRISENC). Verse 24

7. Joseph's brothers' sold him to men who took him to
    ___ ___ ___ ___ ___ (PYTEG). Verse 28

8. Jacob mourned for Joseph by tearing his clothes and putting on
    ___ ___ ___ ___ ___ ___ ___ ___ ___ (CLOKSCATH). Verse 34

From the story of Joseph's life we learn that God keeps His

___ ___ ___ ___ ___ ___ ___ ___ .

Color Joseph's coat of many colors.

GOD CHOOSES MOSES

God appeared to Moses in a bush that was burning. But the bush did not burn up! God told Moses that He had chosen him to lead His people out of slavery in Egypt. So Moses went to Egypt and led the people out of slavery. Later, God revealed the Ten Commandments to Moses on two tablets.

Color the burning bush and the tablets.

GOD'S MERCY AND COVENANTS STUDY SHEET

A covenant is a solemn promise that creates family bonds. Because God loves humanity so much, He entered into a series of covenants with us. These covenants show how God is always merciful and always keeps His promises.

GOD WANTED to be in a loving family relationship with His people from the very beginning. He created Adam and Eve in a family relationship with each other to be a sign of the relationship He wants to have with us. We call this special relationship a covenant.

A covenant is a solemn promise. It creates a sacred bond of kinship, or family relationship. It is made with a promise to give oneself entirely out of love for the other. A covenant is unbreakable, and there are consequences when a person in the covenant fails to keep his part. God cannot fail in His promises to us. Therefore, we can be confident that God's love will always succeed, no matter what.

In the Old Testament, God entered into five major covenants with His people. God drew us deeper into relationship with Him in each covenant. This was fulfilled in the New Covenant in Jesus Christ. Through the Incarnation, God became man and poured out His love for us on the Cross.

God entered into each covenant with a mediator, or the human person who stood in for everyone else who was part of the covenant. God also made a sign for each covenant. These signs were outward representations of God's love for His people at the heart of each covenant.

First, God entered into a covenant relationship with Adam, the first man. His marriage to Eve, the first woman, became the sign of this covenant. Marriage represented the bond of love that God desired to have with His people. In fact, this covenant is the original blueprint for our lives! Because of the temptation of the serpent, Adam and Eve rejected God's love, and sin and death entered the world. God did not leave us in sin and immediately promised us salvation. But we would need to be prepared to be saved.

Next, God entered into a covenant relationship with Noah, who represented his entire family. Through Noah and his faithfulness, God recreated the earth after the Great Flood. The flood waters washed away the wickedness of sin on the earth. God's creation began its journey toward salvation the same way we all do, with baptism. The sign of this covenant is the rainbow, which God placed in the sky to remind His people of His love.

God then entered into a covenant with Abraham, the Father of Faith. Abraham was the leader of a tribe of people who would become God's Chosen People. God made three promises to Abraham that revealed the plan for the rest of salvation: his descendants would inherit the Promised Land and become a great nation; they would become a line of kings with great power; and they would outnumber the stars and bless the entire world. The sign of this covenant is circumcision, which literally marked God's people as belonging to Him.

God fulfilled His first promise to Abraham in the next covenant with Moses. Moses led the Israelites out of slavery in Egypt into the Promised Land. There God would make them a great nation. It was, however, a long journey to freedom. God worked many signs of His unfailing love through Moses. The Law, summed up by the Ten Commandments, was chief among these signs. By the Law, God taught His people the meaning of love.

The last covenant of the Old Testament was with David. This covenant fulfilled God's second promise to Moses. God chose David to be a mighty king who would found a royal dynasty. The sign of this covenant was the Temple, a house for worship. David's son, Solomon, built the first Temple. It was a glorious visible symbol of God's dwelling place on Earth with His people. The covenant with David also prophesied the coming of the Messiah, God's own Son, who would save the world from sin. The Old Testament prophets continued to prepare for the Messiah and make God's loving forgiveness known throughout the world.

Finally, in the fullness of time, or the time of the fulfillment of God's promises, God entered into human history and assumed a human nature in the Person of Jesus Christ. God made His love for us known in the life, Passion, death, Resurrection, and Ascension of His only Son. Jesus willingly gave Himself on the Cross to pay the debt of sin so that we would not have to. His Resurrection defeated death. At the Last Supper, He left us the Eucharist as the everlasting sign of the New Covenant. By receiving the Eucharist, Jesus' true Body and Blood, we become united in Him as the one, holy, catholic, and apostolic Church. In this way, we are made sons and daughters of God and restored to the covenant relationship with God that He desired for us from the beginning.

Fill in the blanks to complete the chart about each covenant.

Adam	One Holy Couple	1. God settled Adam in the Garden of _____. God told Adam to care for it, and called Adam to share in His blessings in the marriage covenant.
Noah	One Holy Family	2. God pledged to keep Noah and his family safe from the _____ waters, and then promised He would never _____the earth again.
Abraham	One Holy Tribe	3. God made Abraham _____ promises: a land (or nation), a name (or dynasty), and a worldwide blessing.
Moses	One Holy Nation	4. The Lord used Moses to lead Israel out of slavery in _____. He gave them the Ten Commandments through Moses, and pledged they would occupy the Promised Land.
David	One Holy Kingdom	5. God made a covenant with David to build a worldwide kingdom. The _____ would come from David's line, and God would establish an everlasting throne with His Son.
Jesus Christ	One Holy Catholic Church	6. God promises eternal life to all who _____.

GOD KEEPS HIS PROMISES
ISAAC AND CHRIST

A *type* is a person or thing in the Old Testament that foreshadows someone or something in the New Testament. The chart on the next page shows some ways that Abraham's son Isaac is a *type* of Jesus Christ. After you've read and thought about them all, cut out the strips and see if you can match them up correctly! Then answer the questions below.

1. How does reflecting on the connection between these two sacrifices help you answer the question: "Why would God ask Abraham to sacrifice his son?"

    _____

    _____

    _____

2. How does knowing the connection between these two sacrifices bring us to a deeper understanding of God's plan for humanity?

    _____

    _____

    _____

3. How does that understanding lead us to a deeper appreciation of God's mercy?

    _____

    _____

    _____

Sacrifice of Isaac	Sacrifice of Christ
Abraham offers his beloved son.	God the Father offers up His beloved Son.
Isaac carries the wood for his sacrifice.	Christ carries His wooden Cross.
Isaac's sacrifice takes place on Mount Moriah.	Christ's sacrifice takes place on Golgotha, which is a hill of Mount Moriah.
Isaac submits to Abraham.	Christ submits to the Father and willingly goes to His death.
God provides the sacrifice (a ram).	God provides the sacrifice (Jesus).
On the third day of their journey, Isaac survives the sacrifice.	Jesus conquers death and rises on the third day.
Isaac is bound to the wood of the altar.	Jesus is nailed to a wooden Cross.
Isaac is conceived with divine help.	By the Holy Spirit, Jesus was Incarnate of the Virgin Mary.
Isaac's mother was assured of God's goodness and omnipotence.	Jesus' mother was assured of God's goodness and omnipotence.

BIBLE PROMISES STAR

On your own paper, trace and cut out your own star like the one below. On the front, write out a Bible verse that tells you God is a promise keeper. On the back, write a prayer asking God to help you believe in His promises.

Bible Verse

WORDS TO KNOW

Below are the words you should know and understand after the lessons this month. Write the definition on an index card so you can remember it.

Believe	To accept as the truth.
Trust	To rely on someone.
Faith	A gift from God as well as our free response to believe what God tells us about Himself and about the world He made.
Theological Virtues	Faith, hope, and love; these virtues come from God and point to Him.
Obey	To do what God tells us to do (and to do what God's representatives – parents, priests, teachers, and so forth – tell us to do).
Creed	All the things that we believe in.
Apostles' Creed	The most important truths about our Catholic Faith written down together. These include many of the truths God wants us to have faith in.

WORDS TO KNOW

(continued)

Divine Revelation	Truths about God that we could never know on our own and that God has chosen to reveal to us.
Mystery	A truth that is above our ability to understand on our own. We believe in a mystery because God has revealed it to us.
Trinity	A mystery that tells us that there are Three Persons in one God.
Sign of the Cross	A Catholic way to begin prayer; it reminds us of our belief in the Trinity of God and in the Passion and death of His Son, Jesus.
Creator	God, who made all things. Only God can make something out of nothing.

IN THE FULLNESS OF TIME

DECEMBER

This month you will explore questions such as:

How did God keep His promise to humanity?

When and how did God Himself enter the world?

Why did God decide to become man?

VERSE OF THE MONTH
LUKE 1:38

Mary said, "Behold, I am the handmaid of the Lord. May it be done to me according to your word." Then the angel departed from her.

SAINT OF THE MONTH
ST. NICHOLAS

St. Nicholas had a generous and happy heart, and he was very devoted in his love for the poor.

Learn more about St. Nicholas on page 79

LUKE 1:38
SCRIPTURE MEMORIZATION

Write out this month's Bible verse on the lines below.

Mary said, "Behold, I am the handmaid of the Lord. May it be done to me according to your word." Then the angel departed from her.

MY ADVENT PLANNER

First Week of Advent: Week of Expectation

Sunday

Read John 1:19-23. Who is the voice of one crying in the wilderness?

Don't forget to light the first purple candle on your Advent wreath!

Monday

Tuesday

Wednesday

Expect great things from God! Draw a picture that shows something you believe God has in store for you.

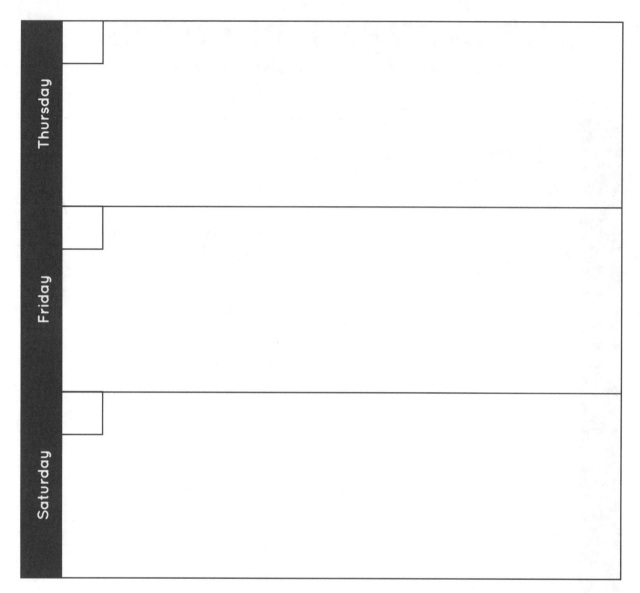

Thursday

Friday

Saturday

REMINDER!

Put your shoes out or hang your stockings
on **December 5** for St. Nicholas to fill!

MY ADVENT PLANNER

Second Week of Advent: Week of Hope

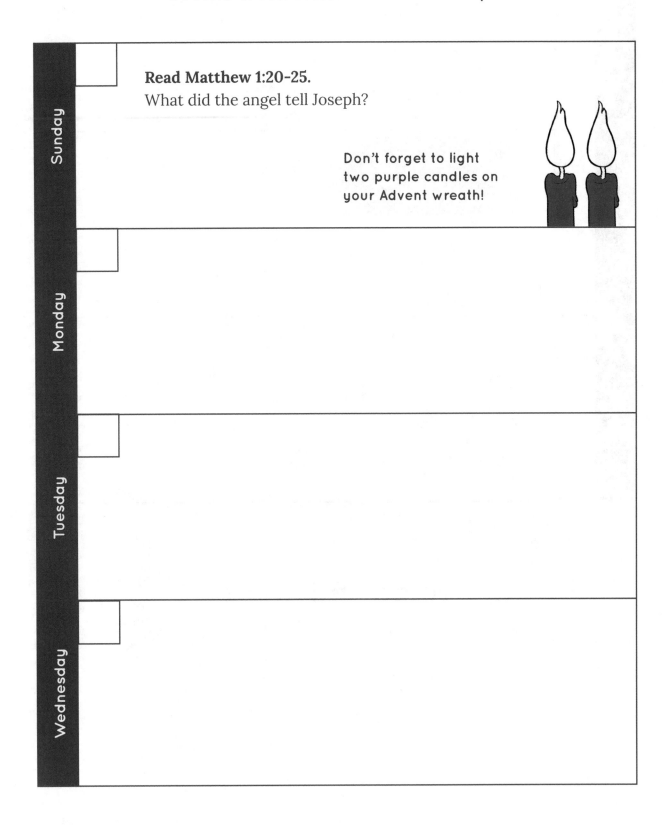

Sunday

Read Matthew 1:20-25.
What did the angel tell Joseph?

Don't forget to light
two purple candles on
your Advent wreath!

Monday

Tuesday

Wednesday

Thursday

Draw Joseph and Mary together at home.

Friday

Saturday

TO DO THIS WEEK

Write a letter to someone you know who is sick or alone.

MY ADVENT PLANNER

Third Week of Advent: Week of Joy

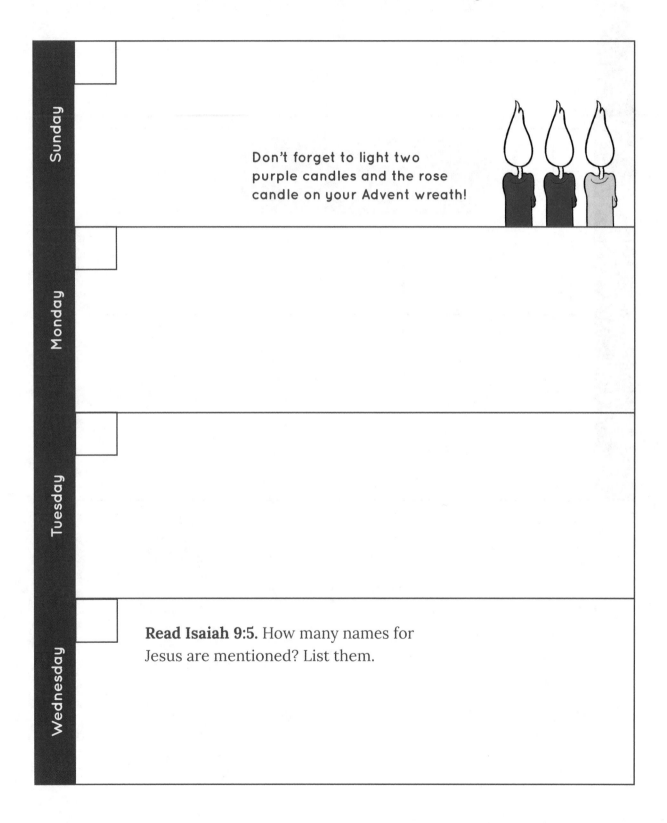

Sunday

Don't forget to light two purple candles and the rose candle on your Advent wreath!

Monday

Tuesday

Wednesday

Read Isaiah 9:5. How many names for Jesus are mentioned? List them.

Thursday

Draw a picture of Jesus and give your picture one of the titles from Isaiah 9:5.

Friday

Saturday

TO DO THIS WEEK

Wrap presents with your parents. Pray for each person as you wrap his or her gift.

MY ADVENT PLANNER

Fourth Week of Advent: Week of Acceptance

Read Luke 2:1-14, and draw a picture of your favorite part of this story.

Don't forget to light all the candles on your Advent wreath!

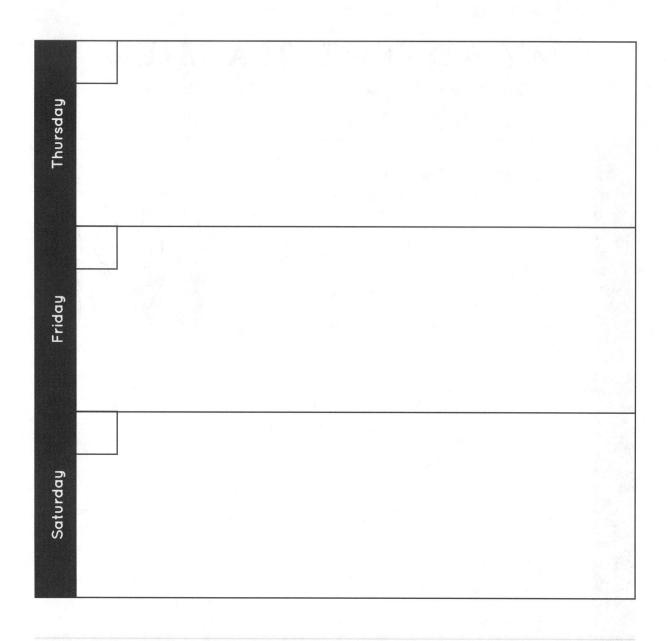

Thursday

Friday

Saturday

TO DO THIS WEEK

Sing Christmas carols with your family.

MARY IS THE NEW EVE

Reflect on the image and discuss the questions as a family,
then pray the Hail Holy Queen prayer together.

Virgin Mary Consoles Eve,
Sr. Grace Remington, OCSO

1. What is the title of this painting?

2. What does it mean to console someone?

3. Eve is on the left. What are some clues you see in the painting that tell you she is Eve?

4. The Blessed Virgin Mary is on the right. What are some clues you see in the painting that tell you she is Mary?

5. Mary is expecting a baby. Who is the baby in Mary's womb?

6. What is Mary doing with her foot?

7. God protected Mary from Original Sin from the moment she was conceived in her mother's womb. This is called the Immaculate Conception. How would you put this in your own words?

8. Would you call this a happy painting? Why or why not?

9. In this painting Mary consoles Eve. How does Mary console all of us?

10. What are some ways you can say yes to God in your own life?

MARY CONSOLES EVE

HAIL HOLY QUEEN

Hail, Holy Queen, Mother of Mercy, our life, our sweetness, and our hope! To thee do we cry, poor banished children of Eve. To thee do we send up our sighs, mourning, and weeping in this valley of tears! Turn, then, O most gracious advocate, thine eyes of mercy toward us, and after this, our exile, show unto us the blessed fruit of thy womb, Jesus. O clement, O loving, O sweet Virgin Mary.

AMEN.

CROSSWORD PUZZLE

Complete the puzzle using words you have learned this year.

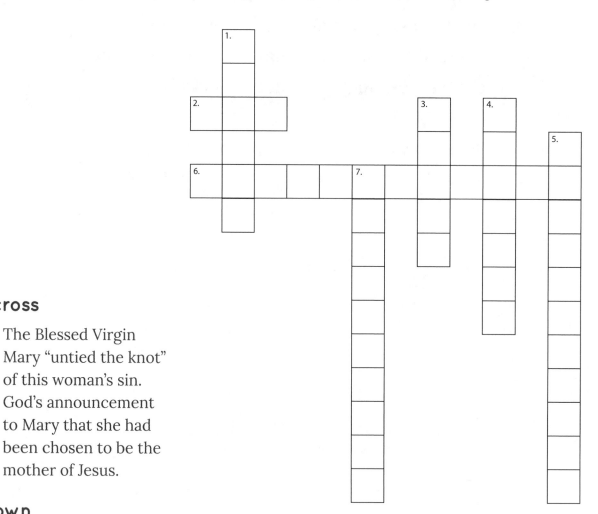

Across

2. The Blessed Virgin Mary "untied the knot" of this woman's sin.
6. God's announcement to Mary that she had been chosen to be the mother of Jesus.

Down

1. Jesus is fully human and fully _____.
3. The angel greeted Mary, "Hail, full of _____."
4. Jesus is the Second Person of the Blessed _____.
5. This word means that God became man (or the Word became flesh).
7. Mary was conceived without Original Sin. This gift God gave her is called the Immaculate _____.

ST. JOHN THE BAPTIST

JOHN 1:19-23

ST. JOSEPH

MATTHEW 1:20-25

ST. NICHOLAS OF MYRA
THE BRINGER OF GIFTS

SAINT OF THE MONTH

A LONG TIME AGO there lived a very special boy whose name was Nicholas. He lived in a country called Lycia, which is now known as Turkey. When Nicholas was about nine years old, both of his parents died. Even though he was alone, he did not feel sorry for himself. Instead, he took the love that he had in his heart for his parents and poured it out on the people around him, especially the poor. Nicholas loved Jesus and always tried to obey Him.

When Nicholas was a boy, he knew a man with three daughters. Each of the girls wanted to be married, but they couldn't marry because they did not have money saved. (At the time, the families of daughters were expected to pay money to the men they would marry. These payments were called dowries.) The girls' father was very poor and desperate. He feared he would have to sell his daughters as servants. When Nicholas heard of this father's problem, Nicholas knew Jesus would want him to help.

Nicholas found great joy in giving gifts. But Nicholas gave gifts only secretly. He gave them secretly because he believed it was more pleasing to Jesus to do it that way. So he went out at night when it was very dark with a bag of money. When he got to the house where the father and his three daughters lived, he tossed the bag of money in through an open window. The bag fell into a stocking that had been hung by the window to dry. When the father and daughters found the money the next morning they were so happy. Now the oldest daughter had a dowry and could get married!

Another night, Nicholas did the same thing for the second daughter. And still no one knew where the money came from. With one daughter left to be married, the father was determined to find out who this bringer of gifts was. So on another night, as Nicholas quietly crept up to the window and tossed in a third bag of money, the father caught him! Nicholas tried to run, but he was not quick enough. His gift was no longer a secret. Nicholas asked the father to keep his secret, and he did. So for many years nobody knew who had helped his three daughters.

When Nicholas grew up, his love for Jesus led him to become a priest. He later became the Bishop of Myra. Like all the bishops of the fourth century, Nicholas wore a red robe with white trim and a matching skullcap.

People in Europe remembered Nicholas's generosity long after he died in A.D. 343. People in Holland especially loved St. Nicholas, whom they called Sinterklaas. Dutch children (children from Holland) began a tradition of leaving their shoes by the fireplace or on a windowsill the night before his feast day. They would wake the next morning, December 6, to find gifts he had left them.

Dutch immigrants brought St. Nicholas's story to America, and he became associated with Christmas. This is why the Santa Claus of today wears a red suit trimmed with white fur, with a red cap, and why we hang stockings by the chimney on Christmas eve.

His feast day is December 6.

ST. NICHOLAS OF MYRA

81

WORDS TO KNOW

Below are the words you should know and understand after the lessons this month. Write the definition on an index card so you can remember it.

Annunciation	God's announcement to Mary that she had been chosen to be the Mother of the Son of God.
Immaculate Conception	The unique gift that God granted to Mary, making her free from Original Sin from the moment of her conception.
Incarnation	The truth that the Second Person of the Blessed Trinity (the Son of God) entered time and took on a human nature.
Hypostatic Union	The joining of the human and the divine in Jesus Christ. He is both fully God and fully man.

82

© SOPHIA INSTITUTE PRESS

JESUS: THE WAY, THE TRUTH, AND THE LIFE

JANUARY

This month you will explore questions such as:

Who is Jesus?

What can we learn from Him?

What does He teach us about getting to Heaven?

What is Baptism?

VERSE OF THE MONTH
JOHN 3:16

For God so loved the world that He gave His only
Son, so that everyone who believes in Him might
not perish but might have eternal life.

SAINT OF THE MONTH
ST. PAUL THE APOSTLE

At first, St. Paul was one of Christianity's
worst enemies. But God turned him
into the greatest missionary ever.

Learn more about St. Paul on page 100

JOHN 3:16
SCRIPTURE MEMORIZATION

Write out this month's Bible verse on the lines below.

For God so loved the world that He gave His only Son, so that everyone who believes in Him might not perish but might have eternal life.

_____

_____

_____

_____

_____

_____

_____

_____

_____

_____

WHO IS JESUS?

Read the essay below, then talk with your parents about the ways we can know God.

At the time of the fulfillment of God's promises, The Son of God assumed a human nature in the Person of Jesus Christ. God made His love for us known in the life, Passion, Death, Resurrection, and Ascension of His only Son.

While His Sacrifice on the Cross took away our sins and defeated death, it is not the only part of Christ's life that is important. On the contrary, everything Jesus did gives us a model for how to live. The Apostles' Creed does not give us details of Jesus' life before His Passion and Crucifixion, but the Gospels do. The Gospels are the books of Matthew, Mark, Luke, and John — the four books of the Bible that tell the story of Jesus' life.

In the Gospel of John, Jesus tells us, "I am the way and the truth and the life" (14:6). Through His life, Jesus reveals to us the truth of who He is, the life He has planned for us, and the way we are to live in order to spend eternity with Him in Heaven. As the *Catechism of the Catholic Church* says: "All that Jesus did and taught from the beginning until the day he was taken up to Heaven is to be seen in the light of the mysteries of Christmas and Easter" (CCC 512).

Who is Jesus?

The Israelites did not expect that the promised Messiah would be God Himself. God revealed this truth to the people. Beginning at the Annunciation, the angel revealed to Mary that the child born to her would be the Son of God. "He will be great and will be called Son of the Most High....Therefore the Child to be born will be called holy, the Son of God" (Luke 1:32, 35).

In addition to sending His angel, God the Father also spoke to the people, and the Holy Spirit was made manifest. As we learned in October, God is the Blessed Trinity: one God in Three Divine Persons — the Father, the Son, and the Holy Spirit. Therefore, Jesus is God — He is one with the Father and the Holy Spirit.

How do we know Jesus is God?

This truth is revealed to us in Matthew's Gospel, where the sacred author describes the moment during Jesus' baptism that the Blessed Trinity together proclaimed Jesus: "[H]e came up from the water and behold, the heavens were opened [for him], and he saw the Spirit of God descending like a dove [and] coming upon him. And a voice came from the heavens, saying, 'This is my beloved Son, with whom I am well pleased'" (Matthew 3:16-17). God the Father spoke those same words at the Transfiguration, with the addition of a command: "This is my beloved Son, with whom I am well pleased; listen to him" (Matthew 17:5).

We also know Jesus is God because, as we will learn more in the next lesson, Jesus performed miracles. Jesus performed many signs and wonders during His public ministry so people would see that He is God and believe in Him.

And finally, we know Jesus is God because, as we see in the Gospel of Mark, He had the power to forgive sins. Since all sin is an offense against God, only God can forgive sins.

HUNTING FOR MIRACLES

Listen as your parent reads the story of how Jesus healed
the blind man in John 9:1-12, and then color the picture.

Listen as your parent reads the story of how Jesus calmed the wind and the seas in Matthew 8:23-27. Draw a picture of the most exciting part of this story.

Listen as your parent reads the story of Jesus bringing a little girl back to life in Matthew 9:18-19, 23-26. Draw a picture of how the girl's father must have felt when Jesus did this!

JESUS' MIRACLES

Jesus performed miracles as a sign of God's love. There are different categories of miracles, but they all demonstrated that Jesus is God. Read the given stories of Jesus' miracles and write a brief summary of each story. Then identify which type of miracle it is: supply, healing, nature, or casting out demons.

Jesus' Miracles

Miracle	Summary	Type
1. Matthew 8:1-4		
2. John 2:1-11		
3. Mark 8:22-26		

Miracle	Summary	Type
4. Mark 4:35-41		
5. Luke 9:10-17		
6. Luke 4:31-37		
7. John 6:16-21		
8. Luke 5:1-11		
9. Mark 5:35-43		

JESUS FORGIVES SINS

Listen as your parent reads the story of Jesus forgiving the sins of the paralyzed man in Mark 2:1-12. Then draw two faces: one that shows how the person felt before he was forgiven and one that shows how he felt afterward.

Remember that God loves us and wants to forgive our sins!

REDEMPTION GAME

What did you lose in the Redemption Game? _____

How did you feel when you lost this item?

☹ 😐 🙂

How did you feel when you got it back?

☹ 😐 🙂

What did you "redeem" for one of your family members? _____

How did your family member who lost that item feel when it was gone?

☹ 😐 🙂

How did he or she feel when it was returned?

☹ 😐 🙂

How did it make you feel to be able to return it to that family member?

☹ 😐 🙂

How do you think God felt when humanity was lost to Him?

☹ 😐 🙂

How do you think He felt when Jesus redeemed humanity?

☹ 😐 🙂

How do you feel about what Jesus did for us?

☹ 😐 🙂

LOOK IT UP AND FILL-IN-THE-BLANKS

Ephesians 2:4-5

But God, _____, because of the great love He had for us, even when we were dead in our transgressions, brought us to life with Christ (by grace you have been saved).

Catechism of the Catholic Church, no. 604

By giving up his own Son for our sins, God manifests that his plan for us is one of benevolent _____, prior to any merit on our part: "In this is love, not that we loved God but that he loved us and sent his Son to be the expiation for our sins."

Romans 5:6-8

For Christ, while we were still helpless, yet died at the appointed time for the ungodly. Indeed, only with difficulty does one die for a just person, though perhaps for a good person one might even find courage to die. But God _____ in that while we were still sinners Christ died for us.

Choose one of the quotations above and re-write it in your own words:

_____

_____

_____

_____

_____

JOHN 3:16 CREATIVE PROJECT

Think about the most important thing or person in the world to you. What or who is it? Draw a picture of yourself that shows how happy you are with that thing or person.

Now imagine that you had to give this item away or lose this person. Draw a picture of how you would feel.

Think once more about how much you love your favorite item or person. Now imagine the love you feel multiplied over and over forever! That is how much God the Father loves Jesus!

Jesus returns the Father's love with all that He is. The love between the Father and the Son is so strong and so amazing that it is another Divine Person: the Holy Spirit!

Color the picture of God the Father, Jesus, and the Holy Spirit together.

God gave His only Son for us, so that whoever followed Him
could go to Heaven. Jesus took our punishment for us.

You would probably feel sad if you had to give
away what was most precious to you.

But even though Jesus suffered, He was happy. He was happy because
He was suffering for you, so that you could go to Heaven and be with
Him forever. Now think about how much this means God loves YOU!

**Color the picture of Jesus and the children. See how much He
loves you and how happy you will be together in Heaven!**

BAPTISM: THE FIRST STEP ON THE WAY

Read the essay below, then talk with your parents about Baptism.

As we have learned, Jesus' whole life gives us a model to follow. He allowed Himself to be baptized in order to point us toward the first step on the way to Heaven: Baptism. When we are baptized as Christians, all our sins are forgiven, including Original Sin, and God makes us His adopted children, restoring our inheritance as partakers in His divine life. We are no longer the lost descendants of Adam; we are children of God and part of His Church.

Why Baptism?

Because Original Sin had damaged our nature so much, human beings would have to be made new. Jesus tells us in John 3:5, "Amen, amen, I say to you, no one can enter the kingdom of God without being born of water and Spirit." And nothing can be reborn without dying. For us to become a child of God, we have to die, too—not physically, of course, but spiritually. In the waters of Baptism, God gives us a spiritual death and rebirth. The word *baptize* even means "to plunge."

It is not only in Baptism that God has used water to make corrupted things new. The waters of Baptism are foreshadowed in the Old Testament stories we learned about in November. For example, in the Great Flood, God used water to flood the sinful world and make it new. He parted the waters of the Red Sea so the Israelites could escape from slavery and begin new lives as God's Chosen People. They had to cross the River Jordan before entering the Promised Land.

In Baptism, God also uses water to make corrupt things new: us. We are freed from the stain of Original Sin and are remade as children of God. This truth was revealed in Christ's own Baptism, detailed in the Gospels. When Jesus was baptized, the Holy Spirit descended upon Him, and the voice of God the Father spoke: "This is my beloved Son, in you I am well pleased." Even though we can't see it, this same thing happens at every Baptism. The Holy Spirit pours down, and the Father rejoices in His beloved child.

Why Is Baptism Necessary?

But if Jesus restored our inheritance by dying on the Cross and rising again, why is there still a need for Baptism? Because Original Sin is real, and Jesus Himself gave us this Sacrament to forgive it. And He tells us clearly that Baptism is not just a suggestion: it is a requirement. He allowed Himself to be baptized, and before He ascended into Heaven, He commanded the Apostles to baptize people "in the name of the Father, and of the Son, and of the Holy Spirit." For more than 2,000 years, Christians have administered this Sacrament, using the same words Jesus commanded his Apostles to use.

Like all the Sacraments, Baptism actually brings about what it represents – in this case, spiritual death and rebirth; forgiveness of sin, and the possibility of Heaven. That is one reason we baptize babies. There is no reason we should withhold God's saving grace. And in case of necessity, anyone with the right intention can baptize another person who wishes for it.

Why Is There Still Sin?

So if Baptism forgives Original Sin and makes us children of God, why is there still evil and suffering in the world? And why do we still find it so hard to avoid sin?

Because Baptism *forgives* sin – it doesn't *remove* it. We still live in a world that is broken, and our nature is still weak and wounded. Baptism makes it possible for us to go to Heaven, but we still need to cooperate with grace and live as children of God. That's why even after we are baptized, it's so important to spend time with God in prayer, to listen to the promptings of the Holy Spirit, and to strive to obey God's commands.

Sin is the cause of death, yet Jesus had no sin: He gave himself freely up to death to make it possible for us to be united with God in Heaven for eternity.

KINGDOM OF GOD
MATCHING ACTIVITY

The qualities of the Kingdom of God are listed on the left. Bible quotes that describe these qualities are listed on the right. Match each quote to the quality it describes.

_____ The Kingdom of God is now and is within us.

_____ It is yet to come – in eternity.

_____ It is a priceless treasure. There is nothing worth more.

_____ It is knowledge of God.

_____ It is abundant, full life.

A. The kingdom of heaven is like a treasure buried in a field, which a person finds and hides again, and out of joy goes and sells all that he has and buys that field. Again, the kingdom of heaven is like a merchant searching for fine pearls. When he finds a pearl of great price, he goes and sells all that he has and buys it (Matthew 13:44-46).

B. For behold, the kingdom of God is among you (Luke 17:21).

C. Now this is eternal life, that they should know You, the only true God, and the One whom You sent, Jesus Christ (John 17:3).

D. I came so that they might have life and have it more abundantly (John 10:10).

E. When the Son of Man comes in His glory, and all the angels with Him, He will sit upon His glorious throne, and all the nations will be assembled before Him. And He will separate them one from another, as a shepherd separates the sheep from the goats. He will place the sheep on His right and the goats on His left. Then the King will say to those on His right, "Come, you who are blessed by my Father. Inherit the kingdom prepared for you from the foundation of the world" (Matthew 25:31-34).

ST. PAUL THE APOSTLE
ON THE ROAD TO DAMASCUS

Around the time Jesus was born, a Jewish boy named Saul was born in Tarsus. Tarsus was a Roman city, and so Saul was a Roman citizen. While he was still very young, his parents sent him to Jerusalem to be taught by the greatest rabbi of his time. Saul was an excellent student. He was respected for his great intellect and zeal for the Jewish faith and traditions.

His zeal, however, caused him to feel upset that some Jews were following the New Way, as Christianity was first called. Thinking that he was serving God, Saul became the worst enemy of Christians. He hunted them down and dragged them out of their homes. He imprisoned them and even had them killed. In fact, Saul witnessed the death of St. Stephen, the first Christian martyr. (A martyr is a person who is killed for his Faith.) Those throwing stones at Stephen laid their cloaks at his feet. Because Saul was a leader, it's very likely that Saul had ordered Stephen to be stoned.

One day Saul set out for the city of Damascus. Saul knew there were many new Christians there, and he planned to arrest them and take them back to Jerusalem. The journey to Damascus took about two days by horseback. When Saul and his men were very near the city, they were suddenly surrounded by a light so bright that it knocked Saul to the ground.

We can read the account of what happened next in the book of Acts, 9:4-8:

"He fell to the ground and heard a voice saying to him, "Saul, Saul, why are you persecuting Me?" He said, "Who are You, sir?" The reply came, "I am Jesus, whom you are persecuting. Now get up and go into the city and you will be told what you must do." The men who were traveling with him stood speechless, for they heard the voice but could see no one. Saul got up from the ground, but when he opened his eyes he could see nothing; so they led him by the hand and brought him to Damascus."

Saul could not see for three days, and he didn't eat or have anything to drink. A disciple named Ananias was told by God in a vision to go to Saul, and Ananias obeyed: "[Saul] regained his sight. He got up and was baptized, and when he had eaten, he recovered his strength."

From that time on, Saul went on to preach about Christ. He decided to use his Roman name, Paul, because it would be more familiar to the non-Jews he would be talking to. He met with Peter, our first pope, and some of the other Apostles, to receive Peter's blessing before he started his ministry. Paul spent the rest of his life traveling and spreading the Gospel of Jesus. He established churches and taught other men to lead in his absence. Paul's letters (called epistles) to the churches that he established make up more than one-fourth of the New Testament. He truly is the greatest missionary in Church history!

ST. PAUL THE APOSTLE

WORDS TO KNOW

Below are the words you should know and understand after the lessons this month. Write the definition on an index card so you can remember it.

Love	Choosing to give of yourself for the good of another.
Miracle	An event witnessed by others that cannot be naturally explained and is the result of God's action.
Truth	That which is and should be. God is the fullness of truth.
Baptism	A sacrament Jesus gave us that forgives Original Sin and recreates us as children of God.

CHECK YOUR UNDERSTANDING

In the space below, write any questions you have about all you have been learning. Discuss these questions with your parents so you can find out the answers together.

_____

_____

_____

_____

_____

_____

_____

_____

_____

_____

_____

HE IS NOT HERE; HE HAS RISEN!

This month you will explore questions such as:

Did Jesus really die?

Why is it important that He rose again?

Where is He now?

Will He come back?

VERSE OF THE MONTH
MATTHEW 28:6

"He is not here, for He has been raised just as He said."

SAINT OF THE MONTH
ST. BRIGID OF IRELAND

St. Brigid had a fearless humility. She saw Jesus in every poor person and responded to Him with love even if it annoyed other people.

Learn more about St. Brigid on page 116

MATTHEW 28:6
SCRIPTURE MEMORIZATION

Write out this month's Bible verse on the lines below.

"He is not here, for He has
been raised just as He said."

THE REALM OF THE DEAD

The Harrowing of Hell was painted by Bl. Fra Angelico in 1446.
Look at the painting while you pray the Apostles' Creed
as a family. Then discuss the painting together.

SALVATION IS A PROCESS

Use your Bible to look up the verses below and write them out in the left column. Then explain, in your own words in the right column, what each passage teaches us about salvation.

Write out the verse	What does this passage teach us about salvation?
1 Peter 3:20	
Hebrews 12:14	
Matthew 6:14-15	
John 6:54	
Matthew 19:16-17	
Galatians 6:7-9	

ASH WEDNESDAY
MASS JOURNAL

In the space below, draw a picture or write out a response to your experience at Ash Wednesday Mass. Some questions to think about: What was this Mass like? How was it different from a usual Sunday Mass?

We receive ashes on our foreheads during Ash Wednesday Mass. Color the picture.

TE DEUM

Listen or pray aloud with your parent. Can you make any connections between this hymn and what we've been learning about all year? Feel free to circle words or phrases, write down notes, or draw pictures.

You are God: we praise You;
You are the Lord: we acclaim You;
You are the eternal Father:
All creation worships You.

To You all angels, all the powers of Heaven,
Cherubim and Seraphim, sing in endless praise:
Holy, holy, holy Lord, God of power and might,
Heaven and earth are full of Your glory.

The glorious company of Apostles praise You.
The noble fellowship of prophets praise You.
The white-robed army of martyrs praise You.

Throughout the holy Church acclaims You:
Father, of majesty abounded,
Your true and only Son, worthy of all worship,
And the Holy Spirit, advocate and guide.

You, Christ, are the king of glory,
the eternal Son of the Father.
When you became man to set us free
You did not spurn the Virgin's womb.

You overcame the sting of death,
and opened the Kingdom of Heaven to all believers.

You are seated at God's right hand in glory.
We believe that You will come, and be our judge.
Come then, Lord, and help Your people,
bought with the price of Your own blood,
and bring us with Your saints to glory everlasting. AMEN.

THE ASCENSION

Color the picture of Christ ascending into Heaven.

LAST DAYS AND LAST JUDGMENT

Read the essay below, then talk with your parents about Last Days and the Last Judgment.

The Apostles' Creed tells us that Jesus is seated at the right hand of the Father. The expression "at the right hand of the Father" indicates all the glory that belongs to Jesus and Him alone. We do not have to understand the word *seated* literally. Rather, we can understand it to mean *abiding* or *dwelling* for eternity. Thomas Aquinas wrote that Christ is said to sit at the right hand of the Father because "He reigns together with the Father, and has judiciary power from Him; just as he who sits at the king's right hand helps him in ruling and judging."

Christ's Kingdom is now and is yet to come. Christ reigns now in Heaven, and He also reigns here on earth through the Church, His Body. Since Christ's Ascension, the world has been in what the Church calls the last days, or the time between the Ascension and the Second Coming. Once again, humanity has entered a time of watching and waiting. We do not know the hour of His return, nor can we know it: "But of

that day or hour, no one knows, neither the angels in heaven, nor the Son, but only the Father" (Mark 13:32). But we are called to "Be watchful!" (Mark 13:33).

We must be always watchful, as the Church teaches that "before Christ's Second Coming the Church must pass through a final trial that will shake the faith of many believers" (CCC 675). A person who falsely claims to speak for God will offer people what seems like a solution to their problems, but that "solution" will come at the cost of denying the truth. The Church must pass through this trial, and only then will she enter into the fullness of God's glory. God will bring the victory over evil, and the Last Judgment of the world will then come (see CCC 675-677).

What Is Judgment Day?

At the end of the world, called the Last Judgment or Judgment Day, "Christ will come in glory to achieve the definitive triumph of good over evil" (CCC 681).

At the appointed time, at the end of the world, Jesus will return to this earth to judge the living and the dead and to bring His Kingdom to its fullness. All truth will come to light, the meaning of all creation will be revealed, and individuals will reap what they have sown. How we treated our neighbor will be evidence of whether we accepted or rejected God's gift of grace. Jesus will judge everyone according to His works and will reveal the secrets of every heart. "On the last day Jesus will say to us the words He spoke in Matthew 25:40: 'Truly, I say to you, as you did it to one of the least of my brethren, you did it to me'" (CCC 678). This is the standard by which we will be judged. Ultimately, the Last Judgment will reveal that God's justice triumphs over injustice and that God's love is stronger than death.

But God will not wait until the end of the world to judge each person. At our death, God will immediately judge us. This is called the particular judgment, and we will learn more about it when we study the article of the Apostles' Creed on life everlasting.

THE SHEEP FROM THE GOATS

MATTHEW 25:32

And all the nations will be assembled before Him. And He will separate them one from another, as a shepherd separates the sheep from the goats.

ST. BRIGID OF IRELAND
FEARLESS HUMILITY

"Brigid is her name?"

The King looked at the nervous Kildare chief, Dubhthach.

"Yes," Dubhthach said. "My daughter is one of those who worship the God of that man called Patrick."

"Why do you wish to sell your own daughter to me?" the king continued, looking down from his fortress at the courtyard. "Is she not a hard worker?"

"Yes, King," the chieftain was quick in his reply. "Brigid is a good worker. She grinds the corn, churns the butter, tends to my cows, sheep, and pigs, and is also helpful to guests. She would serve you well, King."

"But there must be something wrong, or you would not be trying to sell her."

Dubhthach said nothing.

"Can it be," said the king, still at the window, "that Brigid is too generous with your goods when it comes to beggars?"

Dubhthach stood up in anger and surprise. He growled, "I admit that is true. But how could you have known this?"

"I see her giving your sword out of your chariot to a leper. That is your chariot, is it not?"

In a rage, Dubhthach dragged Brigid from his chariot. He demanded to know why Brigid thought she could offer such a priceless object to a beggar.

"A priceless object," responded the calm, beautiful girl, "is perfect as a gift to God."

"Be still, Dubhthach," the king said, "this milkmaid's worth before God is greater than any sword."

"Will you take her, then?"

"No. Take her home. Give her her freedom."

Fearless Humility

Some saints are so kind and giving that those who do not believe in the Gospel cannot understand why they act the way they do. This was the holiness of St. Brigid of Kildare, patroness of Ireland.

Brigid was born between A.D. 451 and 453 near Faughart, Ireland. Her mother was a Christian slave who was baptized by St. Patrick. Her father was a pagan chieftain named Dubhthach. Part slave

royal, Brigid responded to the
princess's power.

looked after her kindness.

ilk to a widow, there was,

ough milk left enough

Brigid gave butter to a

s, somehow, enough

gave a sheep to a

master's flocks,

thin.

that her father

for her. But Brigid

herself to Christ alone.

with the young man her father

chosen. She told him that she herself could not marry him. But, she said, if he went into the woods behind her father's house, he would find a beautiful damsel to be his bride. The man followed Brigid's advice and found the woman Brigid had spoken of. He married the woman soon after. It was then that Dubhthach followed the advice of the King of Leinster and gave his daughter her freedom.

Brigid soon gained followers of women who were devoted to a life of service and sanctity in Christ. Brigid determined to form a religious community in the footsteps of St. Patrick.

Legend has it that Brigid then went directly to the King of Leinster to beg for land where she could build a monastery. Standing before the king on a blueberry-covered field in Kildare, Brigid told him

the place where she stood was perfect. The king refused. So Brigid asked God to touch the king's heart. She smiled and said, "Will you at least give me as much land as my cloak can cover?" The king, thinking she was joking, agreed. But Brigid wasn't joking. Brigid handed her purple-red robe to four of her sisters. Instead of spreading it on the ground, they pulled the corners of the cloak and ran in four directions, stretching the cloth over many acres. The king was terrified at the sight and offered the plot of ground to Brigid. The king soon became a Christian and paid for the construction of Brigid's convent. This miracle is the reason for the custom of eating blueberry jam on Brigid's feast day.

Brigid's foundation was well built with stone, earth, and thatch. Smithies, carpenters, kitchens, hostels, chapels, libraries, and monastic cells lined the paths of Brigid's settlement. It served as a thriving center of industry and artistry.

Brigid showed fearless humility: she served others even if it caused others to feel annoyed. This is often the challenge of the Christian life. We are called to respond to Christ Himself as we meet Him in other people, possibly a hundred times a day. As St. Brigid was known to say, "Christ is in the body of every poor man."

ST. BRIGID OF IRELAND

WORDS TO

Below are the words you should know and understand after the lessons this month. Write the definition on an index card so you can remember it.

Descent into Hell	After He died on the Cross, Jesus' soul went to the realm of the dead. There He preached the Gospel to the just who had died before Him.
Resurrection	Jesus came back to life, body and soul. The Resurrection is the crowning truth of our Faith.
Paschal Mystery	The Passion, Death, and Resurrection of Jesus Christ
Ascension	Jesus went up to Heaven 40 days after His Resurrection.
Intercessor	Someone who acts as a go-between.
Judgment Day	The time when Jesus will return at the end of the world to judge the living and the dead and to bring His Kingdom to its fullness.

WORTH TO KNOW

CHECK YOUR UNDERSTANDING

In the space below, write any questions you have about all you have been learning. Discuss these questions with your parents so you can find out the answers together.

I WILL NOT LEAVE YOU AS ORPHANS

MARCH

This month you will explore questions such as:

Who is the Holy Spirit?

What is the Church?

What is the Church's mission, and what
is my part in that mission?

VERSE OF THE MONTH

JOHN 14:18

"I will not leave you as orphans; I will come to you."

SAINT OF THE MONTH

ST. PETER

St. Peter was our first pope. He led and cared
for Jesus' flock until he died a death like Jesus'.

Learn more about St. Peter on page 131

JOHN 14:18
SCRIPTURE MEMORIZATION

Write out this month's Bible verse on the lines below.

"I will not leave you as orphans;
I will come to you."

WHO IS THE HOLY SPIRIT?
READING

As we learned in October, the Holy Spirit is the Third Divine Person of the Trinity. Read more about the work of the Holy Spirit below.

The Holy Spirit in the Old Testament

We can see the Holy Spirit working in the Old Testament. The book of Genesis describes how the Spirit of God moved over the waters of creation. The Father gave life to the first man when He breathed His Spirit into Adam. The Holy Spirit spoke through the prophets in the Old Testament.

The Holy Spirit in the New Testament

We see the Holy Spirit clearly in the New Testament. The Holy Spirit kept the Blessed Virgin Mary from all sin. He conceived Jesus in Mary's womb. Throughout His life, Jesus spoke of the Holy Spirit. After His Resurrection, Jesus breathed the Holy Spirit onto the Apostles. Jesus told the Apostles that He would always be with them and would send the Holy Spirit to them. The Holy Spirit would be poured out on them and give them fortitude. Fortitude is courage that is strengthened by God.

Ten days later, on the feast of Pentecost, Jesus' promise to send the Holy Spirit was fulfilled. The Holy Spirit gave the Apostles all the spiritual gifts they needed to preach the Gospel. This is why we call Pentecost the birthday of the Church. The Church was born in that outpouring of the Holy Spirit. The Church is truly a work of God Himself. People did not create the Church – God did.

The Holy Spirit and the Church

It is in the Church that we know the Spirit's fullness. It is the Spirit who inspires the Sacred Scriptures, preserves the Tradition of the Apostles, intercedes for us in prayer, empowers and sanctifies us through the sacraments, teaches and protects us through the Magisterium, and builds up the Church through His gifts and ministries.

WHO IS THE HOLY SPIRIT?
ACTIVITIES AND PRAYER

The Holy Spirit in the Old Testament

In the beginning, the Spirit of God moved over the waters. The Father gave life to the first man when He breathed His Spirit into Adam. The Holy Spirit spoke through the prophets in the Old Testament.

Color the picture of the Father breathing life into Adam.

The Holy Spirit in the New Testament

On the feast of Pentecost, the Holy Spirit was poured out on the Apostles. The Apostles saw tongues of fire resting upon their heads. The Holy Spirit gave the Apostles all the spiritual gifts they needed to preach the Gospel. This is why we call Pentecost the birthday of the Church. The Church was born in that outpouring of the Holy Spirit. The Church is a work of God Himself. People did not create the Church — God did.

Color the picture of Pentecost.

HAPPY BIRTHDAY
SONGWRITING

Pentecost is the birthday of the Church! Write an original song about Pentecost that can be sung to the tune of "Happy Birthday." Write it on the lines below, and color in the birthday cake.

_____

_____

_____

_____

_____

_____

_____

_____

SYMBOLS OF THE HOLY SPIRIT

Look up the Scripture passages and determine and record which symbol of the Holy Spirit is in each and why you think that it is a symbol of the Holy Spirit.

1. **Matthew 3:16**   Symbol: _____

   Why? _____

2. **Acts 2:3 and Exodus 3:2**   Symbol: _____

   Why? _____

3. **Acts 2:2 and Genesis 1:2**   Symbol: _____

   Why? _____

4. **Matthew 3:11 and John 3:5**   Symbol: _____

   Why? _____

5. **Exodus 16:10**   Symbol: _____

   Why? _____

6. **Acts 10:38 and 1 John 2:20-27**   Symbol: _____

   Why? _____

KEYS TO THE KINGDOM

Look at the papal insignia and then answer the questions that follow.

1. The Church is the visible sign of Christ's Kingdom on earth. The pope is the visible head of the Church on earth. Jesus made St. Peter the first pope. This symbol of the papacy (or the pope's office) is on the flag of Vatican City. You can see it in Roman Catholic churches all over the world. What do you first notice about it?

2. What do you think the crossed keys represent?

3. Why do you think one key is gold and the other silver?

I will place the key of the House of David on his shoulder; what he
opens, no one will shut, what he shuts, no one will open.
—ISAIAH 22:22

And so I say to you, you are Peter, and upon this rock I will build my Church,
and the gates of the netherworld shall not prevail against it. I will give you the
keys to the kingdom of Heaven. Whatever you bind on earth shall be bound
in Heaven; and whatever you loose on earth shall be loosed in Heaven.
—MATTHEW 16:18-19

4. Look at the Bible verses above. How do they connect to each other and to the
    papal insignia?

_____

_____

_____

_____

_____

_____

_____

_____

_____

BONUS: Why do you think the pope's ring is called the Ring
of the Fisherman? (See Matthew 4:18-20 for a hint!)

THE SPIRIT AND THE CHURCH

Match the person or item from the answer bank with each description. Some answers may be used more than once.

Answer Bank

Jesus   The Holy Spirit   St. Peter   The Pope

1. Protects and guides the Church _____

2. The first pope of the Church _____

3. Founded the Church _____

4. Successor of St. Peter _____

5. Reveals to you that Jesus is Lord _____

6. Sent the Holy Spirit at Pentecost _____

7. Preached at Pentecost _____

8. Was poured out at Pentecost _____

9. Third Person of the Trinity _____

10. Prince of the Apostles _____

11. God who became man _____

ST. PETER
PRINCE OF THE APOSTLES

SAINT OF THE MONTH

In the small village of Galilee in the time of Christ lived a fisherman named Simon. Jesus called Simon, his brother Andrew, and ten other men in a very special way. These 12 men became known as the 12 Apostles. When Jesus asked His Apostles who the people thought He was, they said the people thought He was a prophet. Then Jesus asked, "But who do you say that I am?" Simon answered that Jesus was the promised Messiah, the Son of God. Jesus answered Simon, "You are Peter; and upon this rock I will build My Church." Jesus changed Simon's name to Peter. The name Peter means rock, and Jesus built the Church on that rock, with Peter as the first pope. This is why Peter is known as Prince of the Apostles.

Peter was a courageous and faithful man. It took bravery to leave behind his livelihood in order to follow Jesus. But even as he made this choice, he didn't fully understand who Jesus was or what He was calling him to do. Peter's faith grew as he saw Jesus perform many miracles, such as walking on water. But it would take Jesus' death and Resurrection for him really to understand.

When men came to arrest Jesus, Peter cut off a man's ear with his sword, but Jesus healed the man's ear. Jesus warned Peter that Peter would deny Jesus. Peter promised that he would not, but while Peter waited for Jesus, three people asked Peter if he had been with Jesus. Peter lied and said he had not been with Jesus. He denied even knowing Jesus! Then Peter remembered Jesus' prediction and left, weeping.

Peter felt awful for abandoning His Master and Teacher. It would have been easy for Peter to sink into despair. But he didn't. And three days after Jesus was crucified, He rose from the dead. The Risen Jesus came to Peter and the Apostles with love and forgiveness.

Before He ascended into Heaven, Jesus spoke to Peter alone. Jesus asked Peter three times if Peter loved Him, and each time Peter said yes. In answer, Jesus said to Peter, "Feed my sheep" or "Feed my lambs." Jesus told him these things three times as a way of healing Peter's pain for having denied Jesus three times.

After Jesus had ascended into Heaven and the Holy Spirit had descended on the Apostles, Peter was the first Apostle to preach and to work miracles in Jesus' name. With the Holy Spirit to strengthen his natural courage, Peter had the fortitude to preach the Gospel even when being a Christian was illegal and punishable by death. Peter was imprisoned, but an angel freed him and he continued to preach to Jews and to Gentiles.

With St. Paul's help, Peter led the first Church council in Jerusalem. He wrote two epistles, or letters, that are in the New Testament. In the year A.D. 64, the Roman emperor Nero condemned Peter to be crucified. Peter asked to be crucified upside down because he did not feel worthy to die as Jesus did. His relics are in St. Peter's Basilica in Rome.

ST. PETER

THE CHURCH IS THE PEOPLE OF GOD

CREATIVE ACTIVITY

Draw people together in the pews (make sure that you draw yourself!). Draw a priest at the altar.

Draw a picture of yourself being Christ in the world somewhere other than in a church building.

WE ARE THE PEOPLE OF GOD

As a family, discuss the information that follows. As you do, write notes or draw pictures that will help you remember the information.

We are chosen and set apart by God. We belong to Him.

The Greek word for Church is *ekkalein*. It means "to call out." We are called out to be God's chosen people.

The People of God are like a family. We are God's sons and daughters. We have dignity and freedom.

As God's People we have the mission to continue Jesus' work on earth. We must be light and salt to the world.

PRIEST, PROPHET, AND KING

God created us in His image, with different roles to play. These roles are strengthened at Baptism. All baptized Christians are sons and daughters of God, share in Jesus' mission as priest, prophet, and king, and are called to love.

> **Priest** – The main job of a priest is to offer sacrifice. That means that he gives things to God to worship Him.

> **Prophet** – A prophet proclaims God's word to others.

> **King** – A king rules and governs his land and subjects.

What are some ways that you can live out the roles given to you at Baptism?

Priest:

_____

_____

Prophet:

_____

_____

King:

_____

_____

WORDS TO KNOW

Below are the words you should know and understand after the lessons this month. Write the definition on an index card so you can remember it.

Holy Spirit	The Third Divine Person of the Trinity.
Pope	The visible head of Christ's Church; St. Peter was the first pope.
Pentecost	The day Jesus sent the Holy Spirit to the Apostles to give them the spiritual gifts they needed to preach the Gospel. It is the "birthday of the Church."
People of God	Baptized Christians from all over the world who believe in God and follow His commands.
Mystical Body of Christ	The body of believers united with Christ and with each other.
Teach	To preach the Gospel.
Sanctify	To make holy.
Govern	To lead through service.

ONE HOLY, CATHOLIC, AND APOSTOLIC CHURCH

This month you will explore questions such as:

How do we know the Catholic Church is the Church Jesus founded?

What happens after we die?

What does "life everlasting" mean?

VERSE OF THE MONTH
REVELATION 21:5

The One who sat on the throne said,
"Behold, I make all things new."

SAINT OF THE MONTH
ST. CATHERINE OF SIENA

St. Catherine lived during the time of the great plague. Catherine cared for the sick and treated their bodies with dignity.

Learn more about St. Catherine on page 154

REVELATION 21:5
SCRIPTURE MEMORIZATION

Write out this month's Bible verse on the lines below.

The One who sat on the throne said,
"Behold, I make all things new."

THE FOUR MARKS OF THE CHURCH

Read the essay below, then talk with your parents about the marks of the Church.

When we recite the Apostles' Creed, we say that we "believe in the holy catholic Church." This means that we believe that Jesus established one true Church for all of humanity. It is not to imply that other faiths (especially other Christian faiths) do not contain elements of truth. But it is to say that, according to the Vatican Council's Decree on Ecumenism: "It is through Christ's Catholic Church alone, which is the universal help toward salvation, that the fullness of the means of salvation can be obtained."

We know by the Church's four marks (traits or characteristics) – the Church is one, holy, catholic, and apostolic – that the Catholic Church is the Church that Jesus Christ founded. Jesus gives these traits to the Church through the Holy Spirit.

The Church Is Holy

The Church is holy because her founder, Jesus Christ, is holy and because the Church exists to bring all people to salvation in Jesus Christ through the sacraments. This mark of the Church does not mean that the imperfect human beings who make up the Church are all living holy lives. Pope Paul VI explained that the Church is holy, "though having sinners in her midst, because she herself has no other life but the life of grace. If they live her life, her members are sanctified; if they move away from her life, they fall into sins and disorders." The Church is also holy because her mission – to bring all of humanity to salvation in Christ through the sacraments – is a holy one.

The Church Is Catholic

The word *catholic* here means *universal*, in the sense of being whole and complete. Most importantly, the Church is whole and complete because Christ is always with it. St. Ignatius of Antioch said, "Where there is Christ Jesus, there is the Catholic Church." First, the Church has been given the fullness of the truth and is the only means of salvation. Second, the Church is whole and complete because Jesus established His Church for the entire human race. Jesus said, "Go, therefore, and make disciples of all nations" (Matthew 28:19).

The Church Is Apostolic

That the Church is *apostolic* means that the Church was founded by Jesus Christ on the Apostles, and He continues to govern it today through their successors, the bishops. Jesus made the Apostles the first bishops at the Last Supper, giving them a share of His sacred power to celebrate Mass and minister the sacraments for all Christians. The Apostles then passed on these sacred powers and traditions to proven men through the sacrament of Holy Orders. Those men in turn passed them on, and this process continued in an unbroken line to our time. This is why we can say that today's Catholic bishops are the successors of the Apostles. Your local bishop was consecrated by a bishop who was consecrated by a bishop who was consecrated by a bishop (and so on, over a hundred generations), who was consecrated by an Apostle, who was consecrated by Christ at the Last Supper.

The Church Is One

The Church is one because her source—the Trinity—is one. The Holy Spirit unifies all believers with each other in Christ. This mysterious unity is "the essence of the Church" (CCC 813). This mark also refers to the unity of the Church's belief, worship and liturgy, and government. The Catholic Church has always taught the same doctrines, and Catholics can be "at home" in the Family of God at Mass and in the sacraments anywhere in the world. The official language of the Church, Latin, is a universal and unchanging language. Thirdly, the Catholic Church is one in its submission to the authority of Jesus Christ. Christ promised "one flock, one shepherd" (John 10:16). Christ is the invisible head of the Church, and the pope is Christ's representative on earth, the visible head. Bishops and priests are united to the pope to form one government of Christ's Church.

MARKS OF THE CHURCH FILL-IN-THE-BLANK

Fill in the blanks with a word from the answer bank.
Some words may be used more than once.

| four | twelve | true | apostolic | holy |

| catholic | one | holiness | fullness | Apostles |

1. We believe that the Catholic Church is the true Church founded by Jesus Christ in which the _____ of the truth can be found.

2. There are _____ marks of the Church.

3. These marks are the way in which we can identify the _____ Church founded by Jesus Christ.

4. The four marks are: _____, _____, _____, and _____.

5. The Church was founded by Jesus Christ and exists to bring people to salvation and holiness through the Sacraments and especially the Eucharist. This is a sign of the Church's mark of _____.

6. The Church is _____ because it is for all people, at all times, and possesses the fullness of truth and revelation.

7. To say that the Church is apostolic is to say that it was founded by Jesus Christ on His _____ _____, and it continues to teach the same Deposit of Faith.

8. Because the Church is _____, Catholics can be "at home" in the Family of God at Mass and in the Sacraments anywhere in the world.

THREE STATES OF THE CHURCH
READING AND SCRIPTURE ACTIVITY

Read the information below and then answer the questions that follow.

"Those who are pilgrims on earth, the dead who are being purified, and the blessed in heaven, all together [form] one Church" (CCC 962).

The Communion of Saints is made up of the three states of the Church.

1. Those in Heaven: the saints in Heaven are called the *Church Triumphant* because they are fully enjoying the fruit of the victory that Christ has won for them. They are with the Blessed Trinity, and they see God as He is. They intercede in prayer for all of us.

2. Those on earth: the faithful on earth are called the *Church Militant* because we are still fighting the "battle" against the devil and working to bring the world to Christ. We can ask the saints in Heaven to pray for us. We can help one another by our prayers, good works, and good example. We can help those in purgatory by our prayers and good works and offer up our suffering on their behalf.

3. Those in purgatory: the souls in purgatory are called the *Church Suffering* because they are being purified so that they may enter Heaven. (The word *purgatory* comes from the word *purge*, which means "to purify.") Souls in purgatory died in God's grace, and they are sure that they will go to Heaven. The souls in purgatory cannot pray for themselves, but they can pray for the faithful on earth.

1. How would you put these three states of the Church in your own words?

   Church Triumphant:

   _____

   _____

   _____

   Church Militant:

   _____

   _____

   _____

   Church Suffering:

   _____

   _____

   _____

2. Why does the *Catechism* call those of us on earth "pilgrims"?
   What is a pilgrim? How does it apply to Christians?

   _____

   _____

   _____

3. Read 2 Maccabees 12:39-46. How does this Scripture show
   us the importance of praying for the dead?

   _____

   _____

   _____

PRAYER OF THANKSGIVING FOR THE CHURCH

Now that we have completed our study of the Church, write a prayer thanking God for the gift of His everlasting presence with us through the Church. Try to include many of the aspects of the Church that you have learned about.

_____

_____

_____

_____

_____

_____

_____

_____

_____

_____

_____

_____

_____

_____

APOSTLES' CREED WRAP-UP

Read the essay below, then talk with your parents about the final articles of the Apostles' Creed.

In articles ten, eleven, and twelve we profess our belief in the forgiveness of sins, the resurrection of the body, and life everlasting.

The Forgiveness of Sins

Only God can forgive sins. Christ cleanses us of Original Sin and all personal sins in Baptism. He gave the Holy Spirit to the Apostles, conferring on them His own power to forgive sins and instituting the sacrament of Penance and Reconciliation: "Receive the Holy Spirit. Whose sins you forgive are forgiven them, and whose sins you retain are retained." (John 20:22-23). Other sacraments, including Anointing of the Sick and especially the Eucharist, forgive sins. We will study the sacraments in depth in volume two of this program. For now, we focus on the truth that there is no sin so terrible that it is beyond God's power or desire to forgive if we ask for His mercy with a contrite heart.

The Resurrection of the Body

When we say we believe in the resurrection of the body, we mean that not only will our souls live forever, but our physical bodies will, too. As we have learned, our bodily death is a consequence of Original Sin. Death is the end of earthly life and allows us to participate in the death of Christ, so we can also share in His Resurrection. Jesus conquered death by His Death and Resurrection, and in His Resurrection is the hope of ours. "Whoever eats my flesh and drinks my blood has eternal life, and I will raise him on the last day (John 6:54). On the Last Day, Christ will raise the bodies of all people from the dead and reunite them with their souls.

Life Everlasting

When we state our belief in life everlasting, we mean that life lasts forever – either in heaven or in hell. While we are alive on earth we can choose to accept or reject God's grace. At our death, we will be judged and enter Heaven (through purification or directly), or hell. This is called the particular judgment. St. John of the Cross said of it, "In the evening of life, we shall be judged on our love."

Those who die in God's grace will live forever in the glory of Heaven: the perfect life with the Blessed Trinity, the Virgin Mary, the angels, and the saints. The glory of Heaven is called the beatific vision because we will be able to contemplate God as He is. "At present we see indistinctly, as in a mirror, but then face to face" (1 Corinthians 13:12). "They will see his face" (Revelation 22:4). Unlike earthly satisfaction or pleasure, which is temporary, in Heaven we will be satisfied in our desire to be satisfied – Heaven is the ultimate end and fulfillment of the deepest human longings, the state of supreme, definitive happiness (CCC 1024).

Some will go to Heaven by way of purgatory. The *Catechism* explains, "All who die in God's grace and friendship, but still imperfectly purified, are indeed assured of their eternal salvation; but after death they undergo purification, so as to achieve the holiness necessary to enter the joy of heaven" (CCC 1030). From the beginning of the Church, Christians have offered prayers and sacrifices for the souls of the departed, including most especially the holy Mass, that they may be purified and attain the beatific vision.

Those who have chosen to reject God's merciful love will live forever in the state of eternal separation from Him. "To die in mortal sin without repenting and accepting God's merciful love means remaining separated from him forever by our own free choice. This state of definitive self-exclusion from communion with God and the blessed is called 'hell'" (CCC 1033). God does not pick certain people ahead of time to send to hell. On the contrary, He wishes for all of humanity to turn away from sin and to live with Him forever in Heaven. A person goes to hell only when he makes a conscious choice to turn away from God and continues in that choice to the very end.

The secrets of every person's heart, and the justice and mercy of God, will be made known to all at the Last Judgment. "But the day of the Lord will come like a thief, and then the heavens will pass away with a mighty roar and the elements will be dissolved by fire, and the earth and everything done on it will be found out" (2 Peter 3:10). On this day, all who have died will rise again. People who had already been given a particular judgment will then go on bodily to their eternal destination: heaven or hell. Christ's Kingdom will come in all its fullness.

QUOTE MATCHING
FORGIVENESS OF SINS, RESURRECTION OF THE BODY, AND LIFE EVERLASTING

Read each quotation below and decide whether it best describes Forgiveness of Sins, Resurrection of the Body, or Life Everlasting. Then write your answer on the line.

1. "When the Son of Man comes in His glory, and all the angels with Him, ...all the nations will be assembled before Him. And He will separate them one from another, as a shepherd separates the sheep from the goats. He will place the sheep on His right and the goats on His left. ...And these will go off to eternal punishment, but the righteous to eternal life." (Matthew 25:31, 32, 46)

   _____

2. "This is good and pleasing to God our savior, who wills everyone to be saved and to come to knowledge of the truth." (1 Timothy 2:3-4)

   _____

3. "If the Spirit of the one who raised Jesus from the dead dwells in you, the one who raised Christ from the dead will give life to your mortal bodies also, through his Spirit that dwells in you." (Romans 8:11)

   _____

4. "Go into the whole world and proclaim the gospel to every creature. Whoever believes and is baptized will be saved." (Mark 16:15-16)

   _____

5. "Whoever eats my flesh and drinks my blood has eternal life, and I will raise him on the last day." (John 6:54)

   _____

6. "What eye has not seen, and ear has not heard, and what has not entered the human heart, what God has prepared for those who love Him." (1 Corinthians 2:9)

   _____

7. "For the Son of Man will come with His angels in His Father's glory, and then He will repay everyone according to his conduct." (Matthew 16:27)

   _____

8. "The Lord does not delay his promise, as some regard 'delay,' but he is patient with you, not wishing that any should perish but that all should come to repentance." (2 Peter 3:9)

   _____

I AM THE ALPHA AND THE OMEGA

COLORING PAGE

"I am the Alpha and the Omega, the first and the last, the beginning and the end" (Revelations 22:13). Alpha (A) and Omega (Ω) are the first and last letters of the Greek alphabet. Can you find them in this picture?

ST. CATHERINE OF SIENA
MYSTIC AND DOCTOR OF THE CHURCH

SAINT OF THE MONTH

CATHERINE was born in Siena, Italy, the second youngest of 25 children. From her youth, she joyfully dedicated herself to prayer and devotion.

At the age of 18, Catherine began living in constant prayer as a hermit. During this time, she attracted many followers who wanted to imitate her way of life. She was granted a vision in which she was spiritually married to Jesus. He placed a ring on her finger that was visible only to her and told her that her faith could overcome all temptations.

After three years in seclusion, Catherine and her followers began to minister to the poor, especially those suffering from the bubonic plague, which took millions of lives in Europe at that time. The disease was so terrible that healthy people would not care for or even touch the victims, leaving the dead unburied in homes and in the streets out of fear that they, too, would become sick if they buried them.

Catherine wanted to be Christ in the world. She knew that Jesus had healed the sick, and shown sick people tender love and mercy. And she knew that our bodies are gifts from God, to be treated as temples of the Holy Spirit. So Catherine would tend to the needs of the plague victims. She would prepare them for death and see that they were buried, often burying them herself. She knew that on the Last Day Christ will raise the bodies of all people from the dead and reunite them with their souls, and so the bodies even of the dead should be treated with respect and dignity.

Catherine also wrote many letters to royalty, nobles, religious, and even the pope. Through her letters, Catherine gained a reputation for wisdom, holiness, and the ability to settle disputes. Catherine played an important role during a turbulent time in Church history with multiple men claiming to be pope. Her devotion to the pope of Rome never wavered. She received many visions and was even given the stigmata, the wounds of Christ.

In 1380, Catherine died of a stroke at the age of 33. She was canonized in 1461 by Pope Pius II and given the title Doctor of the Church in 1970 by Pope Paul VI. This is a special title that means her writings are especially useful to Christians.

ST. CATHERINE OF SIENA

AMEN CREATIVE PROJECT

You probably hear the word amen a lot. This word comes from Hebrew and has no exact translation in English, but we can understand it to mean "so be it." Most often, we say amen at the end of a prayer to show that we believe what has been said. In fact, the word amen comes from the same Hebrew root as believe.

Imagine that when you said amen after a prayer, the word took on a physical form. What color is your amen? Does it have a shape? Is it solid? Heavy? Bright? Dazzling? When you pray the Sign of the Cross or a prayer of thanksgiving, does your amen look different from when you ask God for His guidance in a difficult situation? Why or why not? After thinking about these questions, draw a picture of yourself saying a prayer and draw what your amen looks like.

CLOSING PRAYER

Congratulations! If you have done a good job in all your family activities and all the exercises in this book, you have completed your study of the Apostles' Creed! In the space below, write a prayer thanking God for all that you have learned this year and for all the ways that you and your family have grown closer to Jesus and to one another.

_____

_____

_____

_____

_____

_____

_____

_____

_____

_____

_____

_____

_____

_____

_____

_____

WORDS TO KNOW

Below are the words you should know and understand after the lessons this month. Write the definition on an index card so you can remember it.

Marks of the Church	The traits or characteristics by which we know the Church. The four marks of the Church are: one, holy, catholic, and apostolic.
Holy	Sacred, dedicated to God.
Catholic	Universal in the sense of being whole and complete, and for all nations.
Apostolic	Founded by Christ on the Apostles and governed through their successors, the bishops.
Amen	"So be it." Amen comes from the same Hebrew root as believe.
Particular Judgment	At our death, we will be judged and enter Heaven (through purification or directly) or hell.

May

Talk with your parents about things you can do together to grow in your love for Jesus during the month of May. Write your ideas in the space below.

_____

_____

_____

_____

_____

_____

_____

_____

_____

_____

_____

_____

_____

_____

_____

_____

_____

_____

June

Talk with your parents about things you can do together to grow in your love for Jesus during the month of June. Write your ideas in the space below.

July

Talk with your parents about things you can do together to grow in your love for Jesus during the month of July. Write your ideas in the space below.

_____

_____

_____

_____

_____

_____

_____

_____

_____

_____

_____

_____

_____

_____

_____

_____

_____

_____

August

Talk with your parents about things you can do together to grow in your love for Jesus during the month of August. Write your ideas in the space below.